THE
RAILWAY ENGINEERS

By the same author

THE LOCOMOTIVES OF SIR NIGEL GRESLEY (1946)

BRITISH LOCOMOTIVES AT WORK (1947)

THE RAILWAYS OF BRITAIN (1948)

KINGS AND CASTLES OF THE G.W.R. (1949)

SCOTTISH RAILWAYS (1950)

BRITISH LOCOMOTIVES FROM THE FOOTPLATE (1950)

THE GREAT WESTERN RAILWAY: AN APPRECIATION (1951)

BRITISH TRAINS: PAST AND PRESENT (1951)

THE BOYS BOOK OF BRITISH RAILWAYS (1951)

THE PREMIER LINE (1952)

FOUR THOUSAND MILES ON THE FOOTPLATE (1952)

LOCOMOTIVES OF THE NORTH-EASTERN RAILWAY (1954)

LOCOMOTIVES OF R. E. L. MAUNSELL (1954)

FIFTY YEARS OF WESTERN EXPRESS RUNNING (1954)

1   Isambard Kingdom Brunel, engineer of the Great Western Railway
From a photograph taken in the 'fifties

THE
RAILWAY
ENGINEERS

By O. S. NOCK

B.Sc.(Eng.) M.I.C.E.
M.I.Mech.E.

*". . . to honour their memory
and emulate their memory."*
Locke

London
B. T. BATSFORD LTD

First published 1955

Printed and Bound in Great Britain
by Jarrold and Sons Ltd, London and Norwich, for the Publishers
B. T. BATSFORD LTD
4 Fitzhardinge Street, Portman Square, London, W.1

PREFACE

THE coming of railways more than a hundred years ago brought into being a new race of men. It was a young man's game in which there were no precedents to follow. They started young, dared greatly, and some who had the most brilliant records of achievement died young too. In gathering together their stories and trying to weave them into a single narrative I may be guilty of over-simplifying the issue, at certain stages. But as the tale unfolds, an engineer in present-day practice might well be filled with humility in the face of the stupendous tasks essayed by those young pioneers of 100 to 120 years ago. The story has been confined almost entirely to pioneer work, so that so far as civil engineering and locomotives are concerned it ends around 1850, and with operating equipment about the turn of the century.

I am most grateful to the Council of the Institution of Civil Engineers for the generous help that has been given me by the Institution staff, and for permission to reproduce some historic illustrations. I have also had some valuable help from the librarian of the Institution of Mechanical Engineers. But so far as illustrations are concerned I am most of all indebted to the British Transport Commission for putting at my disposal a vast number of pictures, photographs, and drawings now in the possession of the Historical Relics Section.

Writing a Batsford book is always a delightful task, and I shall recall with pleasure the "field days" Mr. Samuel Carr and I have had together browsing through the many collections of pictures offered to us.

Sion Hill
Bath
Spring, 1955

O. S. Nock

7

BIBLIOGRAPHY

Ahrons, E. L., *The British Railway Steam Locomotive: 1825-1925*, 1927.

Barman, Christian, *Early British Railways*, 1950.

Brunel, Isambard, *Life of I. K. Brunel*, 1870.

Clark, Daniel K., *Railway Machinery*, 1855.

Dendy-Marshall, C. F., *Centenary History of the Liverpool and Manchester Railway*, 1930.

Devey, John, *Life of Joseph Locke*, 1862.

Dickinson, H. W., *James Watt*, 1935.

Dickinson and Titley, *Richard Trevithick*, 1934.

Dickson, Rev. W. E., *Railways and Locomotion*, 1854.

Foxwell and Farrer, *Express Trains, British and Foreign*, 1889.

Gibb, Sir Alexander, *Life of Telford*, 1935.

Helps, Arthur, *Life and Labours of Mr. Brassey*, 1872.

Holcroft, H., *The Armstrongs of the Great Western*, 1953.

Jeaffreson, J. C., *Life of Robert Stephenson*, 1864.

Noble, Celia Brunel, *The Brunels, Father and Son*, 1938.

Pendleton, John, *Our Railways*, 1896.

Prout, H. G., *Life of George Westinghouse*, 1922.

Rennie, Sir John, *Autobiography of*, 1875.

Roney, Sir Cusack P., *Rambles on Railways*, 1868.

Smiles, Samuel, *Lives of the Engineers: Smeaton and Rennie*, 1861-2.

Smiles, Samuel, *Lives of the Engineers: George and Robert Stephenson*, 1861-2.

Vignoles, O. J., *Life of Charles Blacker Vignoles*, 1889.

Wood, Nicholas, *Treatise on Railroads*, 1831.

Young, Robert, *Timothy Hackworth and the Locomotive*, 1923.

CONTENTS

Page

PREFACE   7

BIBLIOGRAPHY   8

ACKNOWLEDGMENT   10

LIST OF ILLUSTRATIONS   11

Chapter

I   THE PRELUDE TO RAILWAYS   15

II   BUILDING THE FIRST MAIN LINES   58

III LOCOMOTIVES AND LOCOMOTIVE MEN   117

IV   SOME GREAT CONSTRUCTIONAL WORKS   164

V   RUNNING THE TRAINS   214

INDEX   253

ACKNOWLEDGMENT

THE Author and Publishers wish to thank the following for permission to reproduce the illustrations appearing in this book:

British Railways, Western Region, for Figs. 37, 52 and 53; The British Transport Commission (Historical Relics Section), for Figs. 6, 9, 12, 15, 16, 20–22, 27–30, 43, 44, 49, 56–60 and 62; The Locomotive Publishing Company, for Figs. 35, 36, 41 and 42; The National Portrait Gallery, for Fig. 2; *Picture Post* Library, for Figs. 1, 10, 18, 19, 46–48, 50 and 61; The Director of the Science Museum, South Kensington, for Fig. 3.; The Westinghouse Brake and Signal Company for Figs. 63–65; John S. McLean, Esq., for Fig. 38.

Figs. 4, 7, 40, 54 and 55 are reproduced from originals in the Library of the Institution of Civil Engineers; Fig. 14 from the original in the possession of Frank T. Sabin, Park House, Rutland Gate, London, S.W.7; Fig. 13 from an original in a Private Collection.

LIST OF ILLUSTRATIONS

Figure		*Page*
1	Isambard Kingdom Brunel, engineer of the Great Western Railway	*Frontispiece*
2	George Stephenson	21
3	Nicholas Wood	21
4	Suspension Bridge on the Middlesbrough extension of the Stockton and Darlington Railway	22
5	Trevithick's Newcastle Locomotive	32
6	Stockport Viaduct: Manchester and Birmingham Railway	45
7	Conference of Engineers at Britannia Tubular Bridge	46
8	Stephenson and Losh type of rail joint	49
9	Charleston Viaduct, Manchester and Leeds Railway	63
10	Robert Stephenson	64
11	Olive Mount Cutting	80
12	Sonning Cutting, near Reading: a timber trestle bridge	89
13	Iron bridge over the Trent	89
14	Bathford Bridge, G.W.R.	89
15	Blasting the rocks near Leighton Buzzard	90
16	Building the Wolverton Embankment	90
17	The Sankey Viaduct	93
18	Joseph Locke	99
19	Thomas Brassey	99
20	The stationary-engine house at Camden	100
21	Southern entrance to Watford Tunnel	100
22	Pumping machinery at Kilsby Tunnel	100
23	Blisworth Cutting	104

Figure   *Page*
24 Ventilating shafts, Kilsby Tunnel   106
25 On the North Midland line near Ambergate   107
26 Lime Works at Ambergate   108
27 Crewe Station, L. & N.W.R.   113
28 Bath Station, G.W.R.   113
29, 30 Royal Albert Bridge, Saltash, during construction   114
31 Hackworth's *Royal George*   118
32 Hackworth's *Sans Pareil*   120
33 The *Novelty*   122
34 The *Rocket*   123
35 A Beattie express locomotive, London and South
    Western Railway   147
36 Broad gauge express locomotive, Bristol and Exeter
    Railway   147
37 Daniel Gooch, with a model of one of his "Firefly"
    class locomotives   148
38 Stephenson's *Great A*   152
39 The *Great Western*: Gooch's "colossal" locomotive   153
40 Portion of the temporary viaduct erected over the
    River Tyne during construction of the High Level
    Bridge   169
41 A Sinclair express locomotive, Great Eastern Railway   170
42 Bury 0-4-0 with haystack firebox, Furness Railway   170
43 Abbots Cliff Tunnel, South Eastern Railway   183
44 Conway Tubular Bridge under construction   183
45 Shakespeare's Cliff Tunnel and Viaduct, South Eastern
    Railway   184
46 Panoramic view of the Menai Strait   189
47 The huge sculptured lions for the Britannia Bridge
    entrance   190
48 Building of Conway Tubular Bridge   191
49 Construction of one of the tubes of the Britannia Bridge   192

Figure   *Page*

50   Building the Britannia Bridge: a general view of the works   192

51   Penmaenmawr Viaduct and Tunnel   198

52, 53   The replacing of two viaducts on the Falmouth line   201

54, 55   The South Devon line in "Atmospheric" days   202–3

56   Box Tunnel: western end   204

57   St. Anne's Park Tunnel: western end   204

58   Fox's Wood Tunnel, near Keynsha   204

59   The Skew Bridge at Bath   209

60   Wharncliffe Viaduct, near Hanwell   209

61   William Cubitt, engineer of the South Eastern, and of the Great Northern Railway   210

62   C. B. Vignoles   210

63   "Hole in the Wall": an early signal-box at Victoria   227

64   George Westinghouse: inventor of the automatic air brake   228

65   John Saxby: signal and interlocking pioneer   228

Estimate of the Expence of the proposed Rail Road from the Port of Liverpool to the Town of Manchester

	£	s	d
Forming Excavations & embankments . . .	87599	2	5
Bridges & other Masonry	16920	—	—
Stone Blocks at 1/4 each	15957	6	8
Chairs on Pedestals 10lbs each, at 15£ ⅌ Ton .	16028	12	6
Rails 4 lines of 35 lbs. ⅌ yard for 34 miles at 16£10/. ⅌ Ton	61710	—	—
Laying Rails & forming Road for 34 miles at 5/ ⅌ yard	14960	—	—
Fencing the Road	5729	8	—
Gates 400 at 1£10 each	600	—	—
Waggons for making the Road . . .	4000	—	—
Locomotive Engines 20 at 600£ each .	12000	—	—
Boilers on the Road	1500	—	—
Cranes & Machinery at the Wharfs . .	2000	—	—
Warehouses & Offices	25000	—	—
Land	100000	—	—
Surveys & act of Parliament	10000	—	—
Contingencies during the performance of the Work	26595	10	5
£	400.000	—	—

Geo. Stephenson Engineer

February 5: 1825

THE ESTIMATE OF THE COST OF THE LIVERPOOL
AND MANCHESTER RAILWAY.
Signed by Geo. Stephenson.

By courtesy of "The Railway Magazine."

CHAPTER I

The Prelude to Railways

FOR a time, in the difficult years following the overthrow of Hitler, many people living in Great Britain felt that we were descending to the very nadir of our national fortunes. The thoughts of many a keen young man turned to emigration in the hopes of escaping from the restrictions and frustrations of post-war life. More than a century ago the thoughts of a young Northumbrian pitman were running in the same direction. But in 1807–8 war with Napoleon was still raging, and that young pitman had drawn for the Militia; fighter though he was in more than one sense he had no relish for the army, and with a borrowed six pounds he found a substitute. His meagre savings had already been swallowed up in supporting his disabled father, and all thoughts of emigration thereupon faded, for he was then penniless. Today it is indeed difficult to imagine how the face of England, and perhaps even that of the whole world, might have been changed had that young man sailed for America; for his name was George Stephenson(2).

But the face of Britain was already changing, even before the final defeat of Napoleon. It was a sombre world into which George Stephenson was born at Wylam in 1781. Extreme poverty and discontent were rife in England. Further north, the overthrow of the Jacobite rebellion of 1745 had left much of the Scottish Highlands ravaged, and depopulated, while elsewhere removal of the old chieftains and the deliberate breaking up of the clan system left the people starving, leaderless, and idle. Partly to provide employment, and partly to open up the remoter districts, schemes were prepared for a system of new trunk roads and canals throughout Britain. It was in construction of these that most engineering talent of the day was manifested.

15

Mechanical discoveries there certainly had been by the turn of that century. The day of the "mechanics" was coming, even before Waterloo was fought; the inventions of Hargreaves, and Arkwright, no less than those of Watt revolutionised the textile industry, and began to make Britain the workshop of the world. But it was above all the development of communications, by canal and road, that finally set the Industrial Revolution on its early and tempestuous way.

In the latter part of the eighteenth century and in the critical years of endurance in the earlier phases of the Napoleonic wars a number of important engineering developments took place in Britain. They were quite unconnected and each had a limited objective; yet together they contained the germs of the great conception of railways as they took shape from 1830 onwards. First of all there was the fundamental idea of hauling vehicles on smooth rails instead of on a trackless road. The use of some form of rails seems to date back well into the Middle Ages, while Charles E. Lee in his classic work *The Evolution of Railways* has traced references, if not to "rails", as such, certainly to trackways, or rut-ways in Roman times. The routes of these were levelled to secure good running. There are excellent examples of Roman rut-ways in this country. Of rails proper the earliest uses appear to have been in the mines and quarries. In the mid-seventeenth century they were in use at collieries in the Newcastle district. It was found that horses could draw heavier loads if the wagons ran on rails, and in nearly every case those early rails were made of wood. It is thought that they were simple rectangular bars. In contemporary accounts of colliery activities a definite distinction is made between the vehicles that worked on "rail-roads", and those that did not. The former were known as "waggons", whereas the carts used for conveying coal by road were known as "waynes". One may certainly deduce that the distinction lay in the form of wheel—possibly an early form of flanged device to guide the wagon on the rail-way.

A hundred years later rail-ways were in use at the majority of collieries in England. The rails were mostly of oak, and were sent, sawn to size, by sea from the New Forest to the ports of the north-east coast. Naturally, wooden rails tended to wear out quickly, even though the wagon-wheels were also of wood, and experiments were made in using a softer wood as a base with a hard-wearing surface mounted on the top. Thus when renewal had to take place the amount of harder and more expensive material was less. But already others were laying strips of iron along the tops of wooden rails, and one of the earliest instances seems to have been at the Whitehaven collieries, in Cumberland in 1738. About the same time, too, a trial was made of cast-iron rails, though curiously enough these were made of such light construction that they broke under the weight of heavily-loaded coal wagons, and a reversion was made to wooden rails. The use of iron plates mounted on top of standard wooden rails became fairly common in the latter part of the eighteenth century, and this gave rise to the name "plate-layer" for the men who maintain the rail-way. The name flourishes today, though modern permanent way bears little resemblance to the colliery lines of 200 years ago.

For a time the "plate-ways", as they were sometimes called, took another form. Side plates were used in addition to the running surface, so that in effect the wheels ran in iron troughs. Such wheels needed no flanges, and this arrangement was in general effect something approaching a return to the old rut-ways of Roman times. But while they had the advantage that ordinary carts, if correct wheel-gauge, could run on them the vertical flanges were a handicap where a plate-way had to cross a road on the level. The tracks also tended to accumulate stones and mud. It is at this stage that the distinguished civil engineer William Jessop comes into the picture. In 1788 he designed the celebrated edge-rail, which was the first step towards the modern form of permanent way. It was extremely well thought out, having a broad top to act as a running face, a relatively narrow web, while the bottom flange was again broad. These rails were cast in three-foot lengths and to give greater strength at the point midway between the end supports they were fish-bellied when looked at sideways. At the points of support at the ends the bottom flanges were splayed out to give a good support for the fixings.

Rails of this kind were first used on a line built by Jessop in the Loughborough district, brought into use in 1789.

Meanwhile the plate-ways flourished in other parts of the country, particularly in the colliery districts of South Wales, largely because the wagons in use had flangeless wheels and no other type of way would have accommodated them. At the turn of the century Jessop was concerned with a project of even greater significance, none other than the first public railway to be opened in the world. All the various plate-ways, wagon-ways, and rail-ways that had gone before were private, and built for a strictly limited object; but from a half-formed idea of a new canal between Croydon and Wandsworth there came eventually the Surrey Iron Railway, following roughly the course of the River Wandle from Croydon to its point of junction with the Thames. Jessop was the engineer, but instead of using his patent edge-rails the older form of plate-way was used. There was good reason for this retrograde step. The Surrey Iron Railway was a kind of "free-for-all", on which anyone could haul wagons, carriages or other vehicles on payment of the appropriate tolls. Horses, donkeys or mules were specified as suitable forms of motive power, and difficulties that might have arisen from the need for traffic in opposite directions to cross were avoided by making the line double. The plate type of rails were laid on large stone blocks, and although this permanent way would be considered very rough and clumsy by present standards it certainly achieved its object of permitting heavy loads to be pulled along easily.

An extension was projected southwards from Croydon to Godstone. Jessop was again the engineer, but owing to shortage of funds the line only reached Merstham. Primitive though it was that 8½ miles of line from Croydon cost some £45,000. This line is, however, particularly interesting as it was the scene of one of the earliest timed runs on a railway! In 1805, as a result of a wager a horse took a train of 12 wagons, weighing 38¾ tons, a distance of 6 miles in 1 hour 41 minutes. On the return run, presumably with the grade in its favour, the horse drew a load of 55 tons, though the time is not stated. The Surrey Iron Railway, and its extension southward towards Merstham, was the only

line of any consequence on which plate-rails were used in
the nineteenth century, and from Jessop's pioneer work
with the edge-rail many varieties were produced and
patented between 1800 and the commencement of public
railways in earnest in 1830. Many of these varieties were
concerned with methods of manufacture. Cast-iron as a
material could not be considered satisfactory for members
subject to the continual hammering received by rails under
the passage of heavy traffic, though with manufacturing
technique available at the time the ideal shape, as designed
by Jessop, did not lend itself readily to forging. In consequence various simpler forms of wrought-iron rail were
devised, most having some type of bracket attachment for
mounting to the stone blocks, or other supports. But the
way had been clearly pointed by Jessop, and the developments by which his theory became a practical reality belong
to a later period, and we can turn now to the beginnings of
railway motive power.

The early uses of steam had no direct connection with
transport from one place to another, but several of their
uses contributed a good deal towards the advancement of
knowledge of steam and its properties. The chain of development is indeed continuous, if slow, over a period of nearly
a hundred years. In recounting the story one can tend to
over-simplify the various issues, but one of the earliest if
not the earliest practical use of steam was to be found in the
Cornish beam engines of Thomas Newcomen. This itself was
a development that came about in rather an indirect way.
Newcomen was a native of Dartmouth, and at the beginning
of the eighteenth century he was trading there as an iron-
monger. But while that loveliest of west country seaports
was then enjoying a long Indian Summer of shipbuilding
and trading activity there was evidently not enough work
there locally to absorb all of Newcomen's enterprise, and he
journeyed into Cornwall to find other markets for his tools
among the tin-mining community. There the days of surface
extraction of the ores by washing or "streaming" were long
past. The veins had been followed where they went underground, and with the commencement of mining for the tin,
provision had to be made for pumping out the inevitable

water that entered the workings. The earliest methods used for coping with this nuisance amounted to little more than hand baling, and matters had not progressed very much further when Newcomen first went into Cornwall.

Newcomen himself seems to have contributed little original thought to the engine that bears his name. A Frenchman, one Dionysius Papin, could put forward strong claims to be called the inventor of the cylinder and piston, while at Totnes, in 1698, Thomas Savery obtained a twenty-one years' patent for a vaguely-worded proposal to use a similar device for pumping and drainage work. It was Newcomen, working under licence from Savery, who turned these ideas into a practical proposition. In the cylinder, steam was used to push the piston upwards, and then when the uppermost point of the stroke was reached, water was played on the outside of the cylinder, the steam inside condensed, and a partial vacuum created under the piston. This caused the piston to descend. The strokes of the engine were regulated by hand control, and a youth sat all day long alternately turning the steam and water cocks, at the laborious rate of seven or eight strokes a minute. The piston rod was connected to one end of the great horizontal beam, and to the other end was connected the plunger of the pump by which water was raised from the mine.

One of the most amusing stories of the Newcomen engines concerns the improvement accidentally made by Thomas Hollery, one of the youths who had the indescribably tedious job of operating the cocks. While he sat there, hour after hour, he conceived the idea of operating the cocks by a trigger mechanism actuated from the beam. And so, while his supervisor was away he rigged up a Heath Robinson device, which, crude though it was, worked. The lad had no thought of improving the engine or benefiting his employers; his idea was that if the machine could be made to function automatically he would no longer be fettered to his post, but would be free to wander about to indulge in clandestine pranks with others of his kind, and generally enjoy life. In the meantime the engine, freed from the restraint imposed upon it by the regularly-timed hand operation of the cocks, accelerated its working to nearly

2 George Stephenson

*From a portrait
by H. W. Pickersgill*

3 Nicholas Wood

*From a portrait
in the Science Museum,
South Kensington*

4 Suspension Bridge on the Middlesbrough extension of the Stockton and Darlington Railway, erected by Sam Brown, Esq., R.N.

From an engraving after James Dixon

double the previous speed and became much more useful to its owners!

The Newcomen engines were extensively used in Cornwall, but now our scene must be changing from the high moorlands of the west, where many a hilltop was crowned with the characteristic engine-house and stack of a small mine, and where the mines themselves bore names as appealing as the long story of the industry itself: *Seal Hole*, *Godolphin*, *Wheal Rose*, and above all *Ding Dong*. From this country we move to the Firth of Clyde where in the small seaport of Greenock—a mere hamlet then, by comparison with the great naval centres ensconced in the deep estuaries of Devon and Cornwall—a rather frail and delicate child by the name of James Watt was born in January 1736. As a young schoolboy he was considered dull and inept, and apart from one exciting episode when he was ten years old he led a rather sheltered and uneventful existence. In the previous autumn however the second Jacobite rebellion broke out, and Bonnie Prince Charlie swept down from the Highlands like a whirlwind; but every schoolboy knows how the campaign that started with such éclat ended in utter disaster in the following spring, and how the prince went into hiding. Then one day the alarm went round that he had landed in Greenock; up went the hue-and-cry, and a tremendous house-to-house search was made for him. The house of Watt's parents was included among those examined, but though the excitement was soon over it is strange to think that while the last romance of British history was being played out to its tragic end the modern world with its steam engines and that new race of men, the "mechanics", had already begun.

James Watt, for all the skill in handicrafts he developed in later youth, might, however, have lived out his life as no more than a very expert backroom mechanic, but for an incident that occurred after he was installed as mathematical instrument maker at Glasgow University. He grew up with a rather timid, retiring nature, and although he would persevere to the last degree he was certainly not endowed with strong business instincts. Then during the university session of 1763–4, Professor John Anderson asked him to

repair the model of the Newcomen engine which belonged to
the Natural Philosophy Class in the college. It was a job
after his own heart. He knew a little about steam because
he had read of Dionysius Papin's work, and had made a few
minor experiments himself. With his friend Robison he had
discussed the possibility of self-propelled carriages driven by
steam, but the ideas had gone no further than discussion.
He frankly admits knowing nothing about the Newcomen
engine prior to seeing the model, and set about the job of
repair "as a mere mechanician", to quote his own words.
The model was typical of the Cornish beam engine of the
day, and on it the valves were opened and shut automatically
by tappets in a plug, or pump rod hung from the beam. In
addition to its use in mines this type of engine had also been
used for pumping water for towns. In studying its action
and proportions Watt found that the boiler of the model was
not large enough to keep the engine going for more than a
few strokes, and here again the accident that he was examining a model and not an actual engine helped to lead him on
to further investigation.

In the model it was necessary to economise in the use of
steam, otherwise continuous working was impossible; and
yet considerable loss of steam from condensation occurred
at every stroke, because the cylinder was then cold from the
douche of water sprayed on to it to cause condensation for
the downward stroke. How the solution came to Watt, in
one of the classic moments of British engineering, is told by
Robert Hart, an engineer of Glasgow, who had it from the
inventor's own lips some fifty years later. The date was
May 1765:

It was in the Green of Glasgow. I had gone to take a walk on
a fine Sabbath afternoon. I had entered the Green by the gate
at the foot of Charlotte Street—had passed the old washing
house. I was thinking upon the old engine at the time and had
gone as far as the Herd's house when the idea came into my
mind, that as steam was an elastic body it would rush into a
vacuum, and if a communication was made between the cylinder
and an exhausted vessel, it would rush into it, and might be
there condensed without cooling the cylinder. I then saw I
must get quit of the condensed steam and injection water, if I

used a jet as in Newcomen's engine. Two ways of doing this occurred to me. First the water might run off by a descending pipe, if an offlet could be got at a depth of 35 or 36 feet and any air might be extracted by a small pump; the second was to make the pump large enough to extract both water and air . . . . I had not walked further than the Golf house when the whole thing was arranged in my mind.

So came the separate condenser, and with it Watt had climbed the first rung of the ladder to fame. At one stroke he had secured a possible cut in steam consumption to something like one-quarter of its previous volume. But he was a poor man, and had to rely on others for backing; but with the help of staunch and able friends in Scotland he was able gradually to extend his activities, and then at last, in 1768, he met Matthew Boulton. H. W. Dickinson has aptly summed up their respective natures and suggested that it was because of the very dissimilarity between them that such a strong bond of friendship arose. Boulton and Watt! "One the sanguine, optimistic and assured manufacturer; the other, the cautious, pessimistic and diffident craftsman."

Here I need not attempt to trace the brilliant success of that great partnership, but only that part of it that had a bearing upon the developments of the railway locomotive. This phase began in the year 1777, when the firm secured their first order for a pumping engine for one of the Cornish mines. The improved performance over engines of the Newcomen type made it very attractive for duties that involved ever-increasing volumes of water, and ever-increasing depths of shafts. This first installation in Cornwall was considered so important that Watt, accompanied by his wife, travelled down to Truro to be on the spot.

The first order was for the Ting Tang mine, near St. Day, but the first actually brought into service was at Wheal Busy, near Chacewater. "Wheal" is the old Cornish name for a mine and many of the workings where the beam engines were installed had this prefix. It is appropriate, though doubtless quite accidental, that the name of the mine at which the first Watt engine was set to work in Cornwall is perpetuated on a present-day signal box on the Great Western main line to Penzance. "Wheal Busy Signal Box" is 6½ miles west of Truro, though one would imagine very few of the passengers who happen to catch the name as they pass by know the origin of this rather quaint title. Watt in his journal refers to it as "Wheal Bussy". At first Watt had great difficulty in getting the engines going, largely due to inexperience of the men his firm had to employ. They had a much larger engine than that for Wheal Busy down near Marazion at Wheal Union, and a letter to Boulton throws a vivid light on conditions of the day:

> On Friday I went to Wl. Union, where I found them in ye dumps. On Thursday they had attempted to sett ye Engine to work before they had got it ready. I had told them that they had not cold water for above 7 or 8 strokes pr minute. However as there was a great number of spectators, Dudley thought he would show them some what and accordingly sett off at the rate of 24 sts pr minute, he soon got all his water boiling hot and then seemed at a loss why the Engine would not go . . .

Watt devised a novel and ingenious method by which his firm received payment for the engines. He describes it thus:

> Our profits arise not from making the engines, but from a certain proportion of the savings in fuel which we make over any common engine that raises the same quantity of water to the same height. The proportion of savings we ask is one third part to be paid to us annually for twenty five years, or if our employers chuse it, they may purchase up our part at ten years price in ready money.

One might well imagine that such terms were setting the stage for an accountant's paradise, and it was not long before we find Watt imploring Boulton to come down to Cornwall in person to get the business ends of the various installations tidied up. There were naturally complications where the performance of a Watt engine could not be compared directly, as to lift and volume of water, with the Newcomen engine it had replaced; and it was not long before his principle of payment by results, or payment by merit, led to difficulties. The Cornish mine-owners were not able to grasp the idea very readily and consequently they grew suspicious of it. At the same time such was the superiority of Watt's engine that no enterprising management could afford to do without it. Nevertheless it was used with a gradually increasing sense of grievance among the Cornish at their dependence upon Boulton and Watt.

The engine might have had an even longer and less disputed reign in Cornwall, despite this covert opposition; but among the engineers was one Richard Trevithick, whose son, also named Richard, was rapidly coming to the fore as one of the most brilliant young engineers and outstanding personalities of the Cornish Mining Industry. Capt. Dick, as he was known, was only a boy of six when the first Watt engine in Cornwall was set to work at Wheal Busy; but before he was out of his "teens" it was evident that he was the very opposite to Watt in temperament. While no less ingenious as a mechanic he had the fire and dash that the Scotsman lacked. If Watt might be accused of timidity, young Trevithick was enterprising to the point of rashness. But for his association with Boulton, Watt might well have remained little more than a clever back-room mechanic. Trevithick on the other hand would have made a stir in the world in whatever age or circumstances he had been born.

The last years of the eighteenth century were a time of trade depression in the tin-mining industry. It was imperative to make economics, and the Cornishmen began to focus attention more and more upon the yearly premiums they had to pay upon the Watt engines. It was only natural that the more active and adventurous spirits began to seek ways of circumventing the Watt patents. Boulton with his keen business instincts saw which way the wind was blowing, but Watt's reaction to the warning of his partner was merely to rail at the ingratitude of the Cornishmen. Rather than go out for a new and improved engine which would put the Cornish market back into his pocket he seems to have prepared only for a last-ditch defence of his existing patent. This technical inaction on Watt's part gave the more ingenious of the Cornish their chance. There were some skirmishes around the person of a one-time engineman named Bull, who left the service of Boulton and Watt, and went over to the Cornish. At the Ding Dong mine, near Penzance, he erected an engine of his own that was so like Watt's that the firm succeeded in getting an injunction to

2*

restrain him from installing any more imitations. But at the same time it became fairly clear that young Richard Trevithick, if not actually a partner of Bull, was involved at Ding Dong, and from that point onwards he gradually became the most serious thorn in the side of Boulton and Watt. At one time he seemed to be the spearhead of the Cornish opposition; at others the firm seemed to be doing their level best to attract him over to their side.

We can, however, pass the events of the next few years, with their "cut and thrust" over the body of the Watt separate-condenser low-pressure engine, save to mention the expansive working of steam described in a patent of 1782 covering certain improvements in his basic engine. The advantage of expansive working is that economy is effected by cutting off the steam supply to the cylinders after the piston has travelled no more than a fraction of its full stroke. The remainder of the stroke is made by the expansion of the steam imprisoned in the cylinder. Watt himself did not pursue the principle, since there was very little saving to be made when the steam was at no more than atmospheric pressure at the start. All through his life he seemed resolutely opposed to using higher steam pressures, due to an earlier experience of a reservoir bursting. In his earlier experimental days, however, the standards of workmanship were crude and lacked the background of established practice; yet many years afterwards the inhibitions remained, and he clung to the old principles with all the disadvantages of huge pistons and heavy moving parts. One must not forget that when his famous patent on the engine ran out in 1800 Watt was an ageing man of sixty-four years and one could hardly expect him to throw off the mantle of timidity then.

By contrast, Richard Trevithick the younger was a "high-pressure" man in every sense of the word. H. W. Dickinson refers to him as "a volcano of ideas". It was about the year 1796 that he made the acquaintance and won the lifelong friendship of Davies Giddy. That distinguished scholar, who afterwards became President of the Royal Society, wrote of this early meeting with Trevithick: "our correspondence commenced soon afterwards, and he was very frequently in the habit of calling at Tredvea to ask my opinions on various Projects that occur'd to his mind—some of them very ingenious, and others so wild as not to rest on any foundation at all." It was unfortunate indeed for Trevithick that although he had friends in plenty there was not one among them who had the astute business sense of a Boulton. He found a kindred spirit and ready associate in his cousin Andrew Vivian, but they seem to have been too much alike in temperament for a sound business partnership. Yet like many men having a mighty physique Richard Trevithick was unassuming, gentle, and pleasing in his manners—in ordinary society at any rate. In the mines he could be a terror. On one occasion he threatened to throw a recalcitrant colleague down the engine shaft, and as to physical strength the story has been told again and again of the young men at Crane Mine who were trying their strength by throwing a sledgehammer from the door of Smith's shop towards the engine-house wall. Trevithick came up, watched their efforts for a moment and then took the sledge himself; in one swing he sent it flying, not merely across the yard but *over the roof* of the engine house!

Trevithick's first great development that has a bearing on railways was the high-pressure engine. Instead of using steam at atmospheric pressure and using a condenser he used steam raised to the pressure of several "atmospheres", and allowed it to escape after each stroke. By working at higher pressures the cylinders, pistons and all the working parts could be made much smaller, and most of the cumbersome paraphernalia surrounding the Watt engine was no longer needed. From the noise the high-pressure engines made when exhausting they quickly earned the nickname of "puffers". In his early married life Trevithick carried on experiments in the kitchen. Those trials were social occasions, as the recollections of his wife clearly show: "A boiler something like a strong iron kettle was placed on the fire: Davies Giddy was stoker and blew the bellows: Lady Dedunstanville was engine man and turned the cock for the admission of steam." Then again, she told that "Shortly afterwards another model was made which ran round the table, or the room." From such experiments it was but a short step to the first road carriage, which was tried out at Camborne on Christmas Eve, 1801. "Captain Dick's Puffer", as the carriage was known, stuck through shortage of steam.

A week later they were out again, and the engine was going much better until they came suddenly to a gully in the road, and the whole affair turned over. It was typical of Trevithick and Vivian that instead of taking this second disappointment to heart they pushed the engine under some nearby shelter, adjourned to the hotel and treated themselves to a sumptuous meal "and proper drinks". No one thought of the fire in the engine. It was left alight, and after evaporating the water in the boiler, heated the boiler itself red-hot, and as the framing was of timber the whole thing went up in flames, and burned down the shelter too! It was to take far more than that to damp the enthusiasm of Trevithick and Vivian. Their joint patent for the high-pressure engine was granted in 1802, and already they had begun to look much further afield than the tin mines of Cornwall. In August of that year Trevithick was at Coalbrookdale working on an experimental engine having a boiler pressure of the unprecedented magnitude of 145 pounds per square inch, and where Watt had been so nervous as never to venture above the atmospheric pressure of 14.7 pounds, Trevithick on another occasion stated that he did not intend to stop loading an engine until the packing burns or blows out under its pressure!

At the time the high-pressure engine patent was granted a suggestion was made that a demonstration of the "road carriage" should be given in London. Trevithick and Vivian took this suggestion up with a will, and in August 1803 the engine and boiler were sent by sea from Falmouth. The assembling was done at the shop of a Mr. Felton in Leather Lane, and after various preliminary trials, they had a longer, and certainly more eventful, run. Captain John Vivian who rode on the carriage writes thus:

> One day they started about four o'clock in the morning, and went along Tottenham Court Road, and the New Road, or City Road: there was a canal along by the side of the road at one place, for he was thinking how deep it was if they should run into it. They kept going on for four or five miles, and

sometimes at the rate of eight or nine miles an hour. I was steering and Captain Trevithick and someone else were attending to the engine. Captain Dick came alongside of me and said "She is going alright". "Yes" I said "I think we had better go on to Cornwall." She was going along about four or five miles an hour, and Captain Dick called out "Put the helm down, John!" and before I could tell what was up Captain Dick's foot was upon the steering wheel handle, and we were tearing down six or seven yards of railing from a garden wall. A person put his head from a window and called out, "What the devil are you doing there! What the devil is that thing?" . . .

Strange to say no notice of their nocturnal experiments got into the daily Press of the day, and having carried them out Trevithick went no further with the development of steam road carriages.

The demand for the high-pressure stationary engines was however rapidly increasing despite the continued and vigorous opposition from Boulton and Watt. With boiler-making in its infancy it was perhaps inevitable that before long one would burst, and Trevithick's rivals made much of the accident at Greenwich in September 1803. But in taking precautions that such an incident should not recur, Trevithick proposed in future to have two safety valves, and "a lead rivet for the part of the boiler or flue exposed to the direct action of the fire". This latter is of special interest as it was the forerunner of the fusible lead plug fitted in a boiler to give warning of dangerous overheating developing in the fire-box. It was not long after this accident that Trevithick met Samuel Homfray, the South Wales ironmaster, and owner of the Penydaren Ironworks at Merthyr Tydfil. He was a keen businessman, but no less a lover of most kinds of sport. He was admitted to a half-share of the high-pressure engine patent and was soon doing a good deal to advertise and extend its use. But it was in his own works that an epoch-making development took place in 1804— nothing less than the first trial of a railway locomotive. Trevithick was building engines for pumping and other duties, and the idea occurred to him to extend the principle of the road carriage to loads on the plate-way that existed from Penydaren Works to the Canal at Abercynon. Homfray was

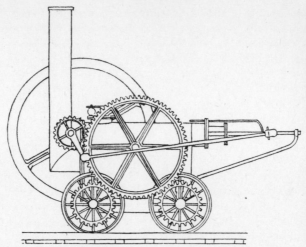

5   Trevithick's Newcastle Locomotive. The Penydaren Engine was similar but the cylinder was in
front of the boiler, and the crankshaft at the rear

keenly in-
terested in
the project,
and gave
Trevithick
every facil-
ity to carry
out his ex-
periments.
He dis-
cussed the
idea with
other iron-
masters in
the district,
some of
whom were
frankly
sceptical,
and it must be admitted that it was more likely on sporting
than technical grounds that Homfray made a bet with
Anthony Hill, proprietor of the Plymouth Ironworks concerning the ability of the "tram waggon", as it was called,
that Trevithick was building.

The task set to the machine was the haulage of 10 tons
of iron on the plate-way from Penydaren to Abercynon Basin
on the Glamorganshire Canal. The distance was $9\frac{3}{4}$ miles
and Anthony Hill bet Homfray 500 guineas even money that
it could not be done. The news of the wager soon got
around, and an intense interest was created in the neighbourhood. It was no more than typical of Trevithick's whole
life that one of the most important developments for which
he was responsible was surrounded by all the excitement of
a purely sporting event. In February 1804 he wrote to
Davies Giddy from Penydaren thus:

> Last Saturday we lighted the fire in the Tram Waggon and
> work'd it without the wheels to try the engine; on Monday we
> put it on the Tram Road. It work'd very well, and ran uphill
> and down with great ease and very manageable. We have
> plenty of steam and power. I expect to work it again tomorrow.

This pioneer steam locomotive, for such it was, had only one cylinder; so like Trevithick's high-pressure pumping engines, with the crank and connecting rod to produce rotary motion, it had a large flywheel to make the motion continuous and avoid stalling on the dead centres. The cylinder was mounted on the back of the boiler, the vertical centre-lines of the boiler and cylinder being coincident. The cylinder was $8\frac{1}{2}$ inches in diameter but had a very long stroke, and extended into the boiler barrel, while the piston rod and the guide for the crosshead projected far out in rear, reminding one of a trombone at its fullest extent. The chimney could not be placed centrally on the front of the boiler due to the presence of the crankshaft, and so it was set over to the left-hand side when seen from the front. The crankshaft was mounted at the front of the boiler and drove the wheels through a train of large gears. The locomotive ran on four wheels, and the gear train was so devised that the last wheel engaged simultaneously with gears on both pairs of running wheels.

As the trials proceeded Trevithick was evidently in high spirits. Again he wrote to Giddy:

> The Tram-Waggon have been at work several times. It works exceeding well, and is much more manageable than horses. We have not try'd to draw but ten tons at a time yet, but I dought not but we cou'd draw forty tons at a time very well for 10 tons stands no chance at all with it . . .

In passing one may comment that Trevithick's grammar and spelling seemed to vary according to the haste or otherwise of the moment of writing. Some of his letters to Giddy are extraordinary if one recalls his innate polish and refinement. In this same letter he continues:

> The publick is much taken up with it. The bet of 500 Hund. Guineas will be desided abt the end of this week and your presence would give mee moore satisfactn than you can consive, and I dought not that you will be fully satisfyde for the toil of the journey by a sight of the engine. The steam thats discharged from the engine is turned up the chimney abt 3 feet above the fire, and when the engine is working 40 st. pr mt., $4\frac{1}{2}$

ft. stroake, Cylinder 8¼ In Diam, not the smallest particle of steam appears out of the top of the chimney, tho' the Chimney is but 8 feet above where the steam is delivered into it, neither is any steam at a distance nor the smallest particle of water to be found. The fire burns much better when the steam goes up the Chimney than what it do when the engine is Idle . . .

The trial for the wager took place on Tuesday, February 21st, 1804. Giddy was not able to be present, and Trevithick wrote thus:

Yesterday we proceeded on our journey with the engine, we carry'd ten tons of iron, five waggons, and 70 men riding on them the whole of the journey. Its above 9 miles which we perform'd in 4 hours & 5 mints, but we had to cut down some trees and remove some large rocks out of the road. The engine, while working, went nearly 5 miles pr hour, there was no water put into the boiler from the time we started untill we arriv'd at our journey's end. The coal consumed was 2 Hund . . . .

Thus Homfray won the bet, and a triumph it was for Trevithick. But although there were many who realised what possibilities were latent in steam locomotive haulage, and although the Press notices were most enthusiastic it is evident that the Penydaren locomotive had many immediate shortcomings. It was not until March 1804 that Giddy found an opportunity to travel down into South Wales and see it for himself, and then his keen practical examination noted a number of points for criticism. Recollecting his visit, and referring to it in some reminiscences written thirty-five years later he comments:

. . . on the 24th. the Engine which Trevithick had constructed for going on the Rail Way, travelled from Penydaren, Mr. Homfray's, to Works called Plymouth & back again; but all the weight was accummulated on the same four Wheels, with the engine, for none of us once imagined, if the weight were divided that the Wheels of the Engine Carriage could possibly hold. In consequence of this great pressure, a large number of rails broke, & on the whole the Experiment was considered as a failure.

Failure it may have been, but Trevithick had got astonishingly near to a remarkable success. It is curious, with a man of Giddy's intellect and perception to guide him, that the possibilities of railway locomotion were not pursued much further. A second locomotive, very similar to that tried at Penydaren, was built in 1805 for use at Wylam Colliery in Northumberland. The man mainly responsible was a mill-wright named Steele who had worked for Trevithick. But this engine, like its predecessor, was too heavy for the track and did very little work at all. This second engine was, however, extremely important, not to Trevithick but to the development of the locomotive itself; for its builder came to know George Stephenson, and passed on to him much of the experience he had gained in the service of Trevithick.

The rather poignant story of how Trevithick himself, having progressed so far, drops out of the picture of railway engineering development is not quite ended with the Peny-daren and the Newcastle locomotives. His indefatigable energy was taken up in projects of all kinds, from an experimental steamboat, steam dredging, excavating at the entrance to the East India Docks, to a first attempt at a tunnel under the Thames. When the latter scheme ended in failure, he turned for one brief moment back to the loco-motive, and in *The Times*, of July 8th, 1808, there appeared the following:

We are credibly informed that there is a Steam Engine now preparing to run against any horse, mare, or gelding that may be produced at the next October Meeting at Newmarket; the wagers at present are stated to be 10,000 l; the engine is the favourite. The extraordinary effect of mechanical powers is (*sic*) already known to the world; but the novelty, singularity, and powerful application against time and speed has created admiration in the minds of every scientific man. TREVITHICK, the proprietor and patenter of this engine, has been applied to by several distinguished personages to exhibit this engine to the public, prior to its being sent to Newmarket; we have not heard this gentleman's determination yet; its greatest speed will be 20 miles in one hour and its slowest rate will never be less than 15 miles.

The engine was certainly shown to the public, but the contest against a racehorse never took place, very likely because the London exhibition came to a premature end.

Trevithick's latest locomotive, nicknamed "Catch-me-who-can", ran on a circular track somewhere near the site of Torrington Square. This demonstration took place in 1808, and it was his last connection with railways.

Trevithick's eccentricity of character, and his unpredictable way of switching from one thing to another was clearly shown at this stage of his life; for while farseeing men were beginning to realise a little of what railways might eventually mean to the country he did not pursue his own achievements, although he was then in the very prime of life. There was William James, for example, a civil engineer of great influence and wealth, who had promoted railways for mines and estates. With the development of steam locomotion, through Trevithick's experiments, James proposed, in 1808, the formation of a "General Railroad Company", with a capital of a million pounds. Public opinion at that time was anything but ready for such vast projects; yet James persevered, and years later he was one of the first promoters of the Liverpool and Manchester Railway. As for Trevithick, how he was lured into taking a large contract for pumping engines for silver mines in Peru, how he journeyed there, became engulfed in a revolution and civil war, lost all his equipment and was reduced to penury is another story. He was out of England in all for many years, and might have been away much longer if he had not chanced to meet young Robert Stephenson in Cartagena. This, however, is carrying the tale many years ahead; though with a character like Richard Trevithick one is naturally curious to know more about his own particular story.

If Trevithick himself played no further part in the development of railways in Great Britain some of his descendants came to hold distinguished positions both at home and abroad. He had four sons, one of whom, Francis, became Locomotive Superintendent of the Northern Division of the London and North Western Railway; while of his twenty-three grandchildren, three held posts of major responsibility in the locomotive world. Frederick Harvey Trevithick was Chief Mechanical Engineer of the Egyptian State Railways; another grandson was Locomotive Superintendent of the Madras Railway; while A. R. Trevithick, a son of Francis, was Works Manager at Crewe, L. & N.W.R., and was a candidate for the post of Chief Mechanical Engineer when it fell vacant in 1909. These Trevithicks of the younger generations appear, however, to have filled their various offices in the role of competent executives; among the records existing there is little sign of that blazing pioneer spirit that so characterised their great forbear.

Returning now to the year 1809 a brilliant young inventor, a Frenchman born, but one who had fled from the Revolution to become an American citizen, was vigorously developing a large timber-sawing business in Battersea. This inventor, Marc Isambard Brunel by name, earned Government recognition by the efficient way in which the huge oaks exported from Russia were sawn to the sizes needed for building our great wooden battleships of the Napoleonic wars. In that same year, 1809, he turned his attention to the mass production of shoes for the British Army, and when his methods had been duly approved he received the order to supply the whole army from 1812 onwards. The shoes were duly turned out at the rate of 400 pairs a day. This work may well seem to have no apparent connection with the beginnings of railways, but it so happened that Marc Isambard Brunel had a son, no more than nine years of age at the time of Waterloo, who was to cause a very great stir in the engineering world.

The older Brunel, inventor and individualist though he was, had an attribute that in one important respect placed him head and shoulders above both Watt and Trevithick: he had a flair for organisation on a big scale. The sawmills provided a splendid example of this. It has been calculated that to build one of our 74-gun wooden battleships 2,000 oak trees were required, and some 12,000 tons of timber was arriving at Chatham annually during the Napoleonic wars. Brunel, by careful use of machinery, integrated the whole process of landing the logs, conveying them to his sawmills, and cutting them to the required size. There was no waste effort either by man or machine; as he himself put it, untried combinations were brought to act in unison and harmony. The younger Brunel(1) proved to be very much the "son of his father" in this respect, and thus Marc Isambard, in his sawmills and shoemaking machinery, and the experience gained from them, was probably able to contribute quite a little to organisation of railway construction when it came to be done on a vast scale. A good deal is heard nowadays about the principle of "Work Study" as applied to repetitive processes in industry; Marc Isambard Brunel by his great contributions to the war effort of 1809–15 can be regarded as one of the earliest exponents of that art. As a result of his achievements Brunel was elected a Fellow of the Royal Society in 1814, though his contemporaries usually referred to him as "that eminent and persevering mechanic". Mechanic! As often as not in those days the word was used in a derogatory sense.

The honour conferred upon Brunel was most unusual at that period for any man connected with the more mechanical aspects of engineering. The professional engineers of the day were engaged upon bridges, canals, harbour works, light-houses, and such like, and some men who tended to take a still more exclusive attitude considered even that the sur-veying and building of roads was beneath the dignity of a civil engineer. Among this number was John Rennie. Certainly he had reached the very front rank by the turn of the century, and had a vast amount of work on hand; but his great contemporary Thomas Telford took a very different view. How much the art of engineering and the profession of the engineer owe to the sterling character of Telford is not generally realised. His direct connection with railways was very slight, and in the 1820's his attitude was reactionary; but the part he played towards the establishment of the Institution of Civil Engineers, and the principles he enun-ciated at the time must have influenced many thousands of men who came to be involved in the surveying and building of railways in after years.

Telford himself stepped into the front rank of his profession on his appointment in 1803 as engineer for the Caledonian Canal. The project was such as to fire the imagination, and the fact that it was obsolete before it was completed did nothing to dim the lustre of the achievement. Six years later he was asked to report on a proposed railway from Glasgow to Berwick. Interested parties felt that improved communication was desirable between the rapidly increasing population in Lanarkshire and Lower Clydesdale and the agricultural districts further east. Their products were complementary. Coal and lime were needed in the districts around Peebles, Selkirk, Kelso and lower Tweeddale, while farm produce was needed in Glasgow and the surrounding industrial districts. The "railway" proposed seemed to have been a much elaborated version of the Surrey Iron Railway, and may well have been inspired by the construction of it. Telford was most enthusiastic. He commented at the time: "Nothing which I have before had an opportunity of examining can equal the benefits which are likely to arise from exchanging by a direct and regular conveyance the Coal and Lime which abound in the Western, for the supplies of grain produced in the Eastern Districts . . ." Again the railway was to be a "free-for-all", on which tolls would be charged for the right of persons to haul their own vehicles over its tracks.

Telford surveyed the whole line personally, and estimated a cost of £365,700 0s. 9d.; in passing however one is curious to know what the odd ninepence was for! The link with the Surrey Iron Railway was further suggested when Telford recommended that the plans and estimates should be subjected to an independent check by William Jessop. But here the "canny" instincts of the Scottish promoters asserted themselves, and while appreciating the motives which led Telford to make this suggestion they demurred on account of the delay and expense likely to be involved. Jessop was then living in Derbyshire, and, it was pointed out, was "accustomed to receive very high premiums for his professional labours". Telford, however, managed to meet the objections of the committee by contriving a meeting with Jessop in London, at which the engineer of the Surrey Iron Railway undertook the scrutiny of the Glasgow–Berwick plans for a reasonable fee. After this promising and enthusiastic start, however, the scheme seems to have just faded out.

Telford was much alive to the need for improving communications, though his reports during the first decade of the nineteenth century show him to have been thinking entirely in terms of canals, or haulage by horse on rail-ways.

The experiments of Trevithick, however, had shown how the working at collieries and quarries could be improved by having locomotives that could haul big loads, but the failure of the Penydaren engine through unsuitability of the track led certain engineers on to a false trail. It was thought that in hauling a heavy load, smooth wheels, such as those used by Trevithick, would not grip on a smooth iron rail. Trevithick himself covered the point in his patent, by indicating that the wheels might be made "rough" in some way, so as to provide the necessary grip, but a still more curious invention—curious, that is, when seen in retrospect—was that of Blenkinsop, in 1811, who took out a patent for a toothed-rail laid to one side of the running rail, in which a gear mounted on the axle of the locomotive worked as a pinion in a rack. Such a movement could have resulted in none but slow and cumbersome running, but the Blenkinsop locomotive included one feature that constituted a definite development. It had two cylinders, instead of one as in the Trevithick locomotives, and it was thus possible to dispense with the huge flywheel included in both the Penydaren and the first Newcastle locomotives. The arrangement of two cylinders working cranks at right-angles to each other was due to Matthew Murray of Leeds.

The Blenkinsop locomotives, though clumsy in action, and very slow, achieved a certain reliability in service. From 1812 onwards they were used for haulage of coal from Middleton Collieries to Leeds, $3\frac{1}{2}$ miles, and on occasions one locomotive hauled as many as thirty loaded wagons. They provided the first instance of the regular use of steam locomotives. Before this, experiments had been made at Wylam Colliery, Northumberland, by Mr. Blackett, though the building of Trevithick's "Newcastle" locomotive by Whinfield of Gateshead had ended in failure. But the interest of Mr. Blackett, and his decision to purchase a locomotive of the Blenkinsop type in 1812 inevitably brings the centre of interest in railway development to the Northumberland coalfield. It was to stay there for several years, for it is at this point that George Stephenson begins to enter the picture (2). He does so in a very humble and unobtrusive way. He had been born in the poorest and most obscure of circumstances at Wylam in 1781, and at first all his boyish instincts had been towards a life of farming, or in the care of animals, but inevitably he was drawn towards the collieries, and at fourteen years of age he was appointed assistant fireman at Dewley, at a wage of a shilling a day. The years between 1795 and 1812 were ones of continual struggle against poverty, but in the latter year he was appointed engine-wright at Killingworth High Pit, and it was in the years following this appointment that his direct connection with the locomotive began.

At this point it is important to reflect for a moment upon Stephenson's personal character, for in many ways it provides an explanation of the phenomenal success that came to him in later years. Where Watt, for all his mechanical skill, had been timid, where Trevithick was exuberant, volatile and erratic, Stephenson had the power of calm perseverance. In the years following Waterloo, Britain passed through a period of industrial dislocation and social discontent unparalleled in her history, even including the days of 1945, 1946 and 1947; but in such times while Trevithick was adventuring abroad, and Marc Brunel was caught unprepared for the coming of peace, went bankrupt and was thrown into the debtor's prison, George Stephenson's skill as a mechanic had attracted attention, and through his own character and thrifty habits he was, for those times, a thriving man. His wage, as colliery engine-wright was £100 a year, and he augmented this by mending shoes, repairing clocks, and by making clothes. He was, however, still almost completely illiterate. In 1815 his only son, Robert, went to and from school in Newcastle on a donkey, while George himself went every night to the home of a young friend who had received something of an education, and together they studied books on mechanics.

While the professional rivalries of Telford and the Rennies continued at the exalted levels to which those great engineers had attained, George Stephenson was steadily but surely laying the foundations of his own incomparable reputation. At this stage in his life Stephenson was working on a much smaller and altogether more modest scale than the established leaders of the civil engineering profession; but in the relatively small circle in which he then moved he impressed all not merely by his mechanical ingenuity—great though that was—but by his solidarity, his uprightness of character, and his unceasing devotion to work. In days when he lived at West Moor cottage, in the village of Long Benton, he would often spend a good part of his Sunday walking up and down the colliery railway thinking over the mechanical problems which were taxing the brains of the intelligent workmen of the neighbouring county, while he and many others of his kind used to meet in Newcastle on pay-nights and exchange views on the difficult tasks of the day. George Stephenson had a great capacity for making friends. More than this, he had the rarer quality of being able to adjust his own attitude to the personality of his companion of the moment. I do not mean to suggest by this that he had the quality of two-facedness: it was, that where many men would have reached the pitch of quarrelling when divergencies of views arose Stephenson could keep a tight hold upon himself, and retain the friendship and respect of his companion.

In the years when his position was being slowly consolidated three men in particular came to influence George Stephenson's outlook. Foremost among these was Robert Hawthorn, engine-wright at Walbottle Colliery under whom he had worked as brakesman. Hawthorn was an exacting and often tyrannical supervisor; he appeared to resent the ability of Stephenson and his friend William Locke, and was jealous lest they should progress too far and oust him from his own position. But while Stephenson regarded Hawthorn as "a great enemy", as he recalled in a letter to Locke, written many years later, to quote Jeaffreson:

> he was too prudent openly to quarrel with the cleverest engine-wright of the district. Slowly advancing himself from the position of a brakesman, whose duty it is simply to regulate the action of a steam-engine, to the higher status of a smith, or wright, who mends or even constructs the machine itself, Stephenson stood in frequent need of the counsel and countenance of Hawthorn, then his superior in knowledge, as he was also in age.

In no one of his early relationships is George Stephenson's character shown more clearly than in that with Robert

Hawthorn. William Locke, a fellow workman with him under Hawthorn, became his lifelong friend, though it was chiefly through Locke's brilliant son, Joseph(18), that the spirit and traditions of Stephenson's engineering practice and precepts came later to be carried so far and wide.

The third of those early associates was John Steele, originally a coachman, and afterwards a brakesman on the Pontop mineral railway. Steele was one of those humbly-born north-countrymen who, at the turn of the century, seemed to develop a natural aptitude for figures and mechanical contrivances, and in due course he came to be associated with Richard Trevithick. He assisted in the construction of the famous Penydaren locomotive of 1804, and then returned to the north to build the very first locomotive ever constructed on the banks of the Tyne. This engine was built in Whinfield's Yard, Gateshead, and was intended for use at Wylam Colliery; but unfortunately due to some defects in its construction, and particularly its weight, the locomotive never took up its intended duties. Instead it was used as a stationary engine in an iron foundry in Newcastle. Its construction was nevertheless a piece of pioneer work of great importance, and George Stephenson, both in those informal gatherings of workmen in Newcastle and elsewhere, cultivated the friendship of Steele. He found inspiration in Steele's increasing prophecy and faith in the eventual success of the steam locomotive, and their discussions were always carried forward vigorously on the occasions when Steele visited Stephenson in his home, at West Moor cottage, Little Benton. In Stephenson's eyes here was a man who had worked with Trevithick, and who had himself built a locomotive; yet like Trevithick he was a restless and adventuring spirit and lacked the steadying qualities that enabled Stephenson to progress slowly, with painstaking thoroughness towards the time of his great successes.

But the man who eventually proved instrumental in bringing George Stephenson into the full light of national and international fame was Nicholas Wood(3), the distinguished mining engineer who was viewer at Killingworth Colliery and at several others in the district. Stephenson took a broad view of his duties as engine-wright at Killing-worth. Not only did he keep all the machinery in first class order, but he gave much thought to the transport of coal, both underground and from the pithead to the staiths on the Tyne. Haulage was still laborious despite the existence of a tram road, and the upkeep of the horses was a costly item due to the high price of corn. Stephenson took every opportunity to study the working of the Blackett engines at Wylam and he went to see the Blenkinsop engine running on the Kenton and Coxlodge tram-way. Up to this time there had been many disjointed steps towards the develop-ment of the locomotive, from the early work of Newcomen and Watt, to Trevithick, Murray and Blenkinsop. Now Stephenson was a very clear thinker, and from his careful study of all that had been done before he set out to produce a locomotive that should embody all that was best from the earlier experiments. But a humble engine-wright was in no position to build experimental locomotives on his own account, and so he put his proposals to the lessees of Killing-worth Colliery, in 1813.

The skill with which he had already improved the working of the colliery engines of their various kinds had caught the eye of Lord Ravensworth, and when Stephenson put forth his proposal for locomotive haulage of coal on the tram-way, Lord Ravensworth authorised him to proceed and made the necessary funds available. His first attempt had some resemblance to Blenkinsop's in outward appearance, except that he used smooth wheels on smooth rails. But again the drive was through a series of spur wheels, and the motion was rather jerky, quite apart from the jolts and lurches resulting from the irregularity of the track. This was made worse from the fact that the locomotive had no springs. It was put into service on the Killingworth tram-way in July 1814, and it is recorded that on a special test a load of 30 tons was hauled up a 1-in-450 gradient at 4 miles per hour. Stephenson's advocacy of the steam locomotive was based on the view that it would prove more economical than haulage by horses, but tests at Killingworth did not sub-stantiate this contention, and the speed was no greater. There was another cogent objection to steam, but in

6 Stockport Viaduct: Manchester and Birmingham Railway

From a lithograph by F. Tait, 1845

7 Conference of Engineers at Britannia Tubular Bridge

In centre, Robert Stephenson presides, while *seated*, on right, are Joseph Locke (*front of table*) and I. K. Brunel. *Standing* may be recognised Captain Moorsom (*on extreme left*) with Edwin Clark; Latimer Clark *at table, speaking*; and, *proceeding to right*, Frank Foster, G. P. Bidder, and Captain Claxton, R.N. (*with spectacles*). A. Ross is
From the painting by John Lucas

overcoming this latter Stephenson successfully passed a vital turning point in the history of railways.

As with Trevithick's locomotives, Stephenson used steam at relatively high pressure and exhausted it into the atmosphere. In the first Killingworth locomotive the steam was allowed to escape direct from the cylinders, which of course it did with a sharp hissing noise. This caused horses and cattle to stampede, and a legal action was threatened unless the nuisance was stopped. Instructions were given to the locomotive enginemen to stop their trains when any animals showed signs of taking fright, but the delays resulting from these measures became intolerable. In the meantime Stephenson, thinking round the problem of quietening the exhaust, hit upon the idea of turning the exhaust steam into the chimney; it would then perform a second function, that of increasing the draught upon the fire, but of increasing the rate of ejection of the smoke from the fire and of the hot gases of combustion. Not only was the noise of exhaust practically silenced but the power of the locomotive was greatly increased. The sharper draught on the fire enabled steam to be generated much more rapidly, and made possible much higher speeds. The improved performance in this direction, however, merely brought to light other failings in this first Killingworth locomotive, and in 1815 work was commenced on an improved design embodying the experience gained so far.

In this second Killingworth locomotive Stephenson was concerned particularly with Isaac Dodds, who was the joint patentee. In this machine a great step forward was taken by elimination of all the complicated gear drive, and by connecting the crosshead directly to the driving wheels through the connecting rod. This arrangement was so simple by comparison with earlier mechanisms that one wonders why it was not adopted before; and so, in combination with the successful features of earlier attempts, one now had nearly all the fundamental points of the orthodox steam locomotive: two cylinders, simple direct drive, exhaust turned from cylinders into chimney to increase draught in the fire. This second locomotive was completed in 1815, and its very success in service brought to light other weaknesses

3

in the Killingworth railway system as a whole. Stephenson now saw that if the capacity of his locomotive was to be fully realised radical improvements to the track would be necessary. Thus while he was still responsible for no more than 7 miles of line, he developed his ability as an all-round railway engineer, instead of remaining an engine-mechanic to the exclusion of all else. Naturally, Nicholas Wood, as viewer, had watched all these experiments at Killingworth Colliery, and with increasing regard and appreciation of his engine-wright. While Stephenson grappled with the day-to-day problems, always with the idea of extending locomotive haulage, Wood began to think in a more detached way of problems that were to loom up as railways were built on a larger and more elaborate scale.

Following the completion of the second Killingworth locomotive, Stephenson's principal concern for some little time became the track. Many of the earlier railways had been roughly laid in the first place, and as time went on and the stone blocks sunk under the continual passage of wagons, the going became very rough and unsteady. With wagons of coal it did not matter very much, although the labour of haulage was increased, but with the coming of locomotives the heavier loads accentuated the problems of subsidence, while the roughness of the riding was detrimental to the moving parts of the locomotive itself. The joint between adjacent rails was a source of weakness, and it was this feature in particular that received the attention of George Stephenson. He took the idea of an improved rail-joint and support to a certain Mr. Losh, an enterprising ironfounder in Newcastle. Losh at once saw its possibilities and advanced the necessary money for a joint patent to be taken out in Stephenson's name and his own. The unusual feature lay in the use of a half-lap joint between adjacent rails, instead of butting them as previously. The rails themselves were of cast-iron, and the scarfed joint rested upon a common support. The proprietors of the Killingworth Colliery adopted this new device, and the "Stephenson and Losh" type of rail and joint was substituted for the old cast-iron plate-way, with greatly improved working in consequence.

This invention revealed that Stephenson's acumen extended

well beyond individual
items of machinery, while
in other directions the
theoretical knowledge that
he was gaining by study of
technical books over many
years was beginning to
bear fruit in his wider

8   Stephenson and Losh
type of rail Joint

applications of the principles of steam locomotion. In 1818,
with a view to increasing the efficiency of haulage on the
Killingworth Colliery Railway he carried out, in conjunction
with Nicholas Wood, some tests to determine the resistance of
railway vehicles. Although no doubt Stephenson received a
great deal of help as well as encouragement from Wood it is
astonishing to realise that at so early a date he had conceived the idea of measuring the train resistance by a dynamometer. This latter, in effect a large spring balance, was
of his own design; but it is no less astonishing to read of the
results he obtained, and of the analysis to which he subjected
these results. By later standards his analysis had only a
limited value, since the tests were carried out at the low
speeds then customary. In referring to these experiments
his famous biographer, Samuel Smiles states:

> It was then for the first time ascertained by experiment that
> the friction was a constant quality at all velocities. Although
> this theory had long before been developed by Vince and
> Coulomb, and was well known to scientific men as an estab-
> lished truth, yet, at the time when Stephenson made his
> experiments the deductions of philosophers on the subject were
> neither believed in nor acted upon by practical engineers.

This comment, true enough in itself, might, however, be
capable of misinterpretation. Stephenson quoted three
principal factors contributing to the total train resistance:

(a) friction of axles in the bearings;
(b) friction of wheels on the rails;
(c) the effects of gravity.

At higher speeds, however, a factor of great importance is
the resistance to motion through the air, and this, far from

being constant, increases very approximately in proportion to the *square* of the speed. Air resistance would, however, be practically negligible at the speeds involved in the 1818 tests by Stephenson and Wood; but the pioneer character of this work may be judged from the fact that dynamometer cars, identical in principle to that used by Stephenson, are now used for scientific measurement of train resistance in all kinds of running conditions. The results of the early tests showed how necessary it was to build railways on as level a course as possible, so as to reduce to a minimum the gravity factor of the train resistance and allow the locomotives or horses to pull a maximum load.

The pattern of railways was now beginning to take shape: the track had been greatly improved; steam locomotives were doing steady, regular work, and Stephenson's study of the "mechanics" of a train in motion had given a clear idea as to how future railways should be laid out. All this had, however, been achieved within the narrow confines of the Killingworth Colliery system; these achievements were still virtually unknown, and Stephenson, who was seeking a wider outlet for his energies, once again began to think of emigration. The idea had been put to him by a Mr. Burrel, of Newcastle, but fortunately for the development of railways in this country his reputation had already extended south of the Tyne and in 1819 he was invited to lay out the new Hetton Colliery Railway, a run of about 8 miles to the banks of the Wear near Sunderland. Here Stephenson had to start with a clean sheet, so to speak. The stretch of country from the colliery to the river Wear was very hilly; no more than a limited amount of money was available for building the line, and so the engineer had the severely practical task of applying the principles he had formulated in his studies and experience at Killingworth within the limits of the available capital. To his proved skill as engine-wright was now to be added a severe test of his ability as a surveyor.

The route he planned eventually was an ingenious combination of fairly level stretches, where locomotives could be used, and steep inclines. Some of these latter were self-acting in that full coal wagons descending were made to haul the empty ones up, and at two of the inclines where the self-acting principle could not be applied stationary engines were installed to draw the trains of wagons up. Stephenson provided all the machinery, and at the opening of the line in 1822 there were five locomotives of the Killingworth type in steam. The successful opening of the Hetton Colliery Railway was a milestone in Stephenson's career, but still the speed of haulage by locomotive did not exceed about 5 miles per hour. Nevertheless all the varied threads of development were now being gathered together in one locality, and in one pair of hands, and it is interesting at the same time to look back to the contemporary work of other engineers who were to be most active in the years to come. Among these we may notice particularly Marc Brunel, Telford, John Rennie, and a young soldier named Vignoles, whose promising career in the army had been cut short by the sudden end of the war, at Waterloo in 1815.

For Marc Brunel the end of the war led to financial embarrassment, and eventually a sojourn in the Debtor's Prison. It is indeed a curious commentary upon the times that a man who had rendered excellent service towards the winning of the war, and who had been honoured with an "F.R.S." in recognition of his inventions should share the same indignity and humiliation as a common bankrupt. How his release was at last effected is no part of the story of railway engineering development, but he was restored to freedom in 1821, and in the following year his son Isambard, then sixteen, joined him in his homely little office in Chelsea. Within two years father and son were engrossed in the great and hazardous task of boring the Thames Tunnel. Some years previously a company had been formed—"The Thames Archway Co."—with the same object in view. The advice and assistance of Richard Trevithick had been sought, but the whole enterprise had ended in failure. The renewal of the project, as a practical proposition was due entirely to Marc Brunel's invention of the tunnelling "shield". The idea is said to have come to him almost by accident, and in a strangely picturesque way. One day in the Chatham yard he was examining a piece of timber that had been fairly riddled by the wood-gnawing mollusc, and he noticed the pair of tiny, but very strong shell-valves by which the

creature ate its way into the hardest of wood. As it progressed it was protected by its own shell. From this acute
piece of observation came the idea of the tunnel "shield"—
a framework the shape of the tunnel bore in which the
excavators worked and which protected them from falls of
the ground. It proved indispensable when tunnelling through
soft strata, while a modified and greatly improved version
of this shield was used many years later in the boring of the
deep-level London tube railways.

At an earlier date than Brunel's driving of the tunnel, the
Rennies, father and son, were engaged in bridging the
Thames. John Rennie the elder was a self-made man, but
he rose to fame as a civil engineer comparatively early in
life, and his sons John and George came to inherit a huge
and prosperous business. They were educated in a style
scarcely less than that enjoyed by the nobility of the day;
and of the two John especially entered upon his engineering
life with a decided superiority complex. This is very evident
by his autobiography. Somewhat pompous, not a little self-
righteous, one can quite imagine that he did not mix very
kindly with his brother engineers. In the post-war period
following Waterloo he was busy helping his father with the
Thames bridges, and one after another these splendid structures were opened: Waterloo Bridge in 1817, Southwark
Bridge in 1819, and the new London Bridge some years later,
in 1829. John Rennie the younger was greatly affected by
the death of his father in 1821, and he himself records that
he was in a state of despair and melancholy for about a
month afterwards. He then threw himself so wholeheartedly
into the continuance of his father's work, with bridges,
harbours and drainage works so that it was not until the
Stockton and Darlington line was actually in being that he
enters the field of railways.

The antagonism between the Rennies, as a family, and
Telford, though for the most part covert, comes into the
open from time to time, and is clearly revealed by various
passages in the younger John Rennie's autobiography. After
reaching great eminence himself he is moved to write
patronisingly about one who was without question the foremost engineer of his day, and one whom men came to

England from all ends of the earth to consult. But Rennie wrote of Telford:

He had just finished his great work, the Holyhead Road, with the great connecting suspension bridges at Conway and Bangor, and of which, with good reason, he was justly proud, and could not bear the idea of their being superseded by any other form of locomotion. Although an able engineer in many respects, he was not much of a practical mechanic, and very likely conscientiously thought that railways would not succeed.

The Institution of Civil Engineers was born on January 2nd, 1818. Some of the ablest and more enterprising of the younger engineers of the day were the moving spirits in this development. They sought a means whereby men engaged in the various branches of engineering could meet together, exchange views, and experiences. The term "civil engineer" can be considered to cover any form of engineering other than that for purely military purposes, and it so happened that the men most closely concerned were mainly engaged in the more mechanical aspects of the job. In a single phrase the Institution was founded "for the advancement of mechanical science". It was in 1820 that the founders resolved "That a respectful communication be made to Thomas Telford, Esq., F.R.S.E., Civil Engineer, requesting him to patronise this institution, by taking on himself the Office of President of the same." To the great benefit of the Institution, and of the profession as a whole, Telford accepted, and his views on policy in some ways set a code of conduct for its members. He was determined that the Institution should be for the advancement of engineering rather than of engineers, and while he held the presidential office, as Sir Alexander Gibb has written, there was never any danger of it degenerating either into a trades union or a mere debating society. In engineering practice Telford's opposition to railways had a curious effect after his death. Within the membership of the Institution of Civil Engineers, railway men began to outnumber all others, and although it is carrying this particular part of the story many years forward the "railway mania" brought such a rush of men to be "engineers" that the Institution had a very difficult time with many having no proper qualifications or training putting forward claims to membership.

At about this period a crisis in the affairs of the Institution led to John Rennie being invited to become president, and in his address of 1845 he took the opportunity, once again, to disparage the work of Telford. In view of the part Rennie came to play in railway engineering the comments of Sir Alexander Gibb are worth quoting in full:

It is curious and interesting to see that in the Presidential Address of the following year, which set out to review the whole course of the rise and establishment of Civil Engineering, Telford's part, whether as a contributor to the science of engineering or in the establishment of the Institution is ranked no higher than that of many of his contemporaries. As one reads the Address now, one cannot but feel that its whole object was consciously or unconsciously to establish an earlier origin of civil engineering than Telford. The outstanding figure in Civil Engineering, the father of the profession, is claimed to Smeaton; and it is the Smeatonian tradition, and not Telford that is stated to have provided the vitalising spirit of the new profession. The heat of those far-off controversies and jealousies has long since been dissipated. Their very existence is forgotten; and we can take a more dispassionate view. It is then no disparagement of Smeaton's contribution to engineering, or of the fine example and great contribution he made to the new science, to point out that civil engineering as a recognised profession had no sort of existence until a quarter of a century after his death. All the outstanding figures of that time should receive due praise for their pioneer work. The technical contributions of most of them were important. But the creations of the ideal and ethics of engineering, the establishment of engineers in their own and public estimation, the prestige of the Institution, are due to no one in the way they are due to Telford. He it was who stamped his personality and ideas on the whole profession.

By comparison with Marc Brunel, Telford, and the Rennies in those closing years of the prelude to railways C. B. Vignoles was practically unknown (62). But alone of all his contemporaries Vignoles was not originally intended for the engineering profession. He was a soldier, and was in the thick of the desperate and disastrous night attack on Bergen-op-Zoom, in 1814, in which he was taken prisoner. After the flight of Napoleon to Elba, Vignoles was released and subsequently was ordered to Canada, otherwise he would almost certainly have fought at Waterloo. Then, the end of the war and the disarmament that followed saw him, like many other officers of the regular army, placed on half pay; he sought other employment, and sailed for America where he obtained the post of Assistant State Surveyor for South Carolina. But events were very unsettled in the New World, and after six years of difficulties he returned to England. His son, many years later, quotes an amusing letter relating to his arrival:

On my arrival in town it was five o'clock, and by the time I had got rid of the dust of my journey and made myself decent, it was late in the evening. When I came into the drawing room my aunt looked as black as thunder, which, however, I would not mind. She did not ask me many questions, but lectured me for half an hour on my having borrowed £5 of Mr. M. and an umbrella from Mr. G. But very soon I was "dear Charles", and it ended by her ordering my old room to be got ready for me. . . .

The old lady's father—Charles Vignoles' grandfather— had been an intimate friend of the elder Rennie, and on this, his return to England, the two younger Rennies were among those who came forward with suggestions and help for his future career in England. In two years time he became professionally associated with John Rennie the younger, and so he came to enter the field of railway engineering, with the results to be told later.

Such are no more than a few glimpses of men, hitherto outside the general line of development of steam locomotion and railways, who were to come into contact and conflict with the "mechanics" of the Northumbrian school. And there, centred on Killingworth, the friendship that grew up between Stephenson and Nicholas Wood, based on strong mutual esteem and the bond of good business association may be said to have launched railways into public service, as distinct from their hitherto local and private uses. Wood had the influence and power to back his convictions of Stephenson's soundness as an engineer, and together they watched the progress of the Stockton and Darlington Railway bill through Parliament. Then on April 19th, 1821, the very day that the Act received the Royal Assent, Stephenson and Wood went to Darlington to seek an interview with Edward Pease. As the chief prospector of the line, and the predominant influence in the whole scheme Pease seemed to them to hold the keys to the future of railway development. They were right enough, but that first interview met with only partial success. Stephenson was commissioned to check the original survey of the route, for which the Act was obtained. Many a man in similar circumstances, anxious to secure the major appointment of engineer to this pioneer work would have acquiesced generally to the route authorised the sooner to start on the main job. But George Stephenson was not made that way. As a result of his survey certain modifications were proposed; these made necessary a further bill, with all the opposition renewed, the anxiety increased, and the chances of ultimate rejection never very far away. It was, indeed, not until two years later that the second bill was passed, and then at last, in 1823, Stephenson was appointed engineer-in-chief.

This appointment was verily the turning point in his career. Hitherto his reputation had been local, and although he had laid the Hetton Colliery Railway in 1819 he had been regarded as a skilled mechanic, a tender and builder of engines and machinery rather than an engineer in the broader sense of the word. But the construction of the Stockton and Darlington Railway—of the "road" itself no less than the rails, the machinery and the rolling stock— was a civil engineering enterprise of the first magnitude for those days, and it is no wonder that the leading civil engineers of the day looked with some surprise and envy to the colliery engine-wright of Killingworth who, with the staunch backing of Nicholas Wood, had snatched this glittering prize from under their very noses. The Rennies in particular took this significant event very much to heart, and the result was a battle royal when the next big railway project came up.

But we must return to the year 1821, when George Stephenson was instructed to check the original survey for the Stockton and Darlington Railway; for it was in that

survey that his only son, Robert, was first associated with
him in a railway enterprise(10). Through all his early years
of toil, as a colliery brakesman and then as an engine-
wright, George Stephenson had worked assiduously to edu-
cate his son. There was a difference of no more than twenty-
three years in their ages, and to a large extent father and
son learned from their books together. "Robert must work,
work, as I have worked afore him", his father used to say;
but no father could have been more gratified at the way his
son applied himself to his tasks. On leaving school Robert
Stephenson was apprenticed to Nicholas Wood, and began
work in the Killingworth Collieries; but when his father was
appointed to make the second survey of the Stockton and
Darlington Railway, Robert acted as one of his assistants.
The weather was unusually fine and warm in that early
autumn of 1821, and George Stephenson, John Dixon, and
Robert made a veritable holiday of their congenial task.
They took their frugal meals in the open air; they lodged
at roadside inns, and a vivid sidelight on the proceedings is
thrown by the recollections of Joseph Pease, who was
frequently with them on the job. Pease had referred to
Robert Stephenson—then eighteen years old—as the slight,
spare, bronzed, boy who conversed with his father, both at
the top of their voices in a scarcely intelligible Northumbrian
brogue. There was a bond of the deepest affection between
father and son, and when the survey was completed Robert
Stephenson's name was put upon it, as engineer. This was
done at his father's particular direction.

And now the prelude was ended. The first public railway
was under construction. Many of the pioneer mechanics
who had contributed in varying degrees to the enterprise
that Stephenson so skilfully co-ordinated had passed, or
were passing from the scene: Savery, Newcomen, Watt,
Jessop, Blenkinsop, Matthew Murray and, saddest of all,
Trevithick. The day of "railway engineers" was now at
hand.

CHAPTER II

Building the First Main Lines

THERE is no need to emphasise the pioneer position of the Stockton and Darlington among the railways of this country, or indeed of the whole world. The passing of the bill and the construction of the line were greeted with far more opposition, scepticism, and scorn than enthusiasm, and even among the thinkers of the day one must record that there were many who felt sincerely that it would "never answer". The engine-wright of Killingworth was still no more than a relatively obscure mechanic. But looked at in retrospect, and passing over contemporary details of construction, the Stockton and Darlington Railway stands out as something vastly more than a brave, but rather primitive attempt at railway building. One can laugh at the idea of a man on horseback riding along the line in front of the first train on the opening day, but then just look at the position of the Stockton and Darlington today! The cynics might well say that the promoters laid a foundation far greater than they knew of; but the fact remains that George Stephenson, associated with this enterprise, himself developed a remarkable business sense where railways were concerned. To his detailed skill as a working mechanic and his broader outlook as a surveyor and civil engineer, he gradually acquired a masterly grip on what might be called the grand economic strategy of trade and industry. As I hope to show later the great trunk lines he built did not merely fulfil the needs of some transient boom; they became, and remain, equally today among the most important life-lines of the nation.

In attempting to trace how George Stephenson gradually rose to become one of the outstanding personalities of all time it is interesting to examine in some detail the situation

and traffic possibilities of the Stockton and Darlington
Railway. The focal point of business interest was the rich
coalfield centred upon Bishop Auckland, and from there it
was fifteen miles in a straight line to the nearest point at
which the River Tees was then navigable. The coal owners
sought means of quickening and cheapening transport, and
various proposals for a canal were considered. On one such
project John Rennie the elder was consulted, but for one
reason and another any definite move was postponed time
and again. Once a ready means of transport was provided
business began to develop at both ends of the line. Industries
grew up on both banks of the Tees estuary; with rich ores
in the Cleveland Hills to the south, Middlesbrough, once a
swampy waste, grew into a great ironworking and shipbuilding centre. Then, from the original Stockton and
Darlington line an important extension was carried out west-
ward over the Pennines to provide access to and from the
iron ore districts of Furness and West Cumberland, and a
heavy traffic in coke for the blast furnaces grew up. With
the phenomenal increase in the demand for British coal and
British heavy industrial products, a demand that reached
its climax in the years just prior to the first world war,
traffic between the Bishop Auckland district and Tees-side
grew to such an extent that the North Eastern Railway
electrified the direct line that now connects them.

Some years later George Stephenson said:

The strength of Britain lies in her iron and coal beds; and
the locomotive is destined, above all other agencies to bring it
forth. The Lord Chancellor now sits on a bag of wool; but wool
has long since ceased to be emblematical of the staple commodity
of England. He ought rather to sit on a bag of coals, though it
might not prove so comfortable a seat. Then think [he went on
mischievously] of the Lord Chancellor being addressed as the
noble and learned Lord *on the coal sack*! I am afraid it wouldn't
answer, after all.

Joking apart, Stephenson's homely remarks about the
strength of Britain are as true today as when he uttered
them, and in no districts more thoroughly than those
served by the old Stockton and Darlington line, and in his

own native Northumberland have railways enabled those natural resources to be more fully utilised.

The original route of the Stockton and Darlington Railway was a rather roundabout one. The line ran almost due south from the Bishop Auckland colliery districts to Darlington, and then swung round through very nearly a full right-angle to continue eastwards to Eaglescliff; there it turned north for the last four miles into Stockton. The short cut, straight across country from Shildon to Stockton was built later by the North Eastern Railway; part of it, known as the Simpasture branch, is a purely mineral line over which no passenger service is run. Originally, however, important though the through coal traffic was, the line had obviously to pass through the town of Darlington, and the roundabout route arose in consequence. Today, travellers on the main line from Kings Cross to the North cross the old Stockton and Darlington Railway on a level crossing roughly a mile north of the principal passenger station in Darlington. This portion of the old line, and for about three miles eastward, is not used nowadays by any passenger trains. The present service from Darlington to Stockton and the Tees-side towns is worked over a separate line a mile or so to the south of the old route to Dinsdale, beyond which the mineral line converges. The station on the old line nearby had the picturesque name of "Fighting Cocks". From this point Stephenson's historic route is followed into Stockton.

Two incidents at the time of the inception of the railway throw a vivid light on the conditions of the day. Stephenson and Nicholas Wood had been to Darlington to see Edward Pease, and at the conclusion of a satisfactory interview that astute man asked them casually how they were going to get back to Newcastle that night. "By nip", was the reply, which in modern parlance meant "hitch-hiking"! The only difficulty for Stephenson and his great friend was that there was only one means of conveyance on the roads that night, the evening stage coach, on which it was usually possible to get a lift by tipping the driver. But their talk with Pease had been so long and animated that when eventually they did get out on to the road the coach had passed, and they had to walk the 22 miles to Durham! Such an expedition, however, would have been nothing to Stephenson, who earlier in life had walked the whole way from Montrose to Killingworth. As a result of that interview with Pease, as I mentioned at the conclusion of the preceding chapter, Stephenson was invited to re-survey the line. The directors felt the task ought to be done as quickly as possible, and a special messenger was sent on horseback from Darlington. One can picture the stir his arrival caused in the little mining village of Killingworth, and the stir changed to consternation when the messenger asked the whereabouts of he to whom the letter was addressed. "George Stephenson, Esquire, Engineer." The colliers' wives and the children gathered round excitedly. No such person was known in the village! Repeatedly the hapless messenger enquired; again came the shaking of heads, and at last he was on the point of leaving with the letter undelivered. Then to one of the women came the idea that the letter might be for "Geordie the engine-wright"! They all knew where *he* lived, and in such manner George Stephenson received his first public assignment as an engineer!

The construction of the original Stockton and Darlington line did not involve any very heavy engineering work. Except at the northern end the country was not difficult; but nevertheless the simple and economical route followed was in large measure due to Stephenson's own care and precision in making the survey. With a primitive form of level, of his own make, he did the major part of the sighting himself. During the work he became a familiar and welcome figure in the countryside, with his tall and athletic figure, blue-tailed coat and top boots. With his cheery open face and homely talk he was sure of a welcome in the cottages and farmhouses; but it was characteristic of George Stephenson's innate quality—"one of nature's gentlemen"—that he was just as much at home, and just as welcome in Edward Pease's drawing-room. There one evening he astonished the company by being able to instruct the young ladies in embroidery. Naturally he was asked however he had found the time and opportunity to acquire such skill, and he replied: "When I was a brakesman at Killingworth I learnt the art of embroidery while working the pitmen's buttonholes

by the engine fire at nights." Rarely can there have been
a man who was so astute and far-seeing in business, possessed
of such a diversity of skills with his own hands, and at
the same time so excellent a "mixer" among the great and
the lowly alike.

The track of the Stockton and Darlington Railway was an
item of great importance. It would have been easy enough
for Stephenson to have recommended the use of cast-iron
rails with scarfed joints, for which he had a joint patent
with Mr. Losh. It would, no doubt, have been of immediate
personal profit to himself. But Stephenson was far too
"canny" not to appreciate the merits of something far better
when he saw it, and not many miles to the north of Killingworth, at the Bedlington Ironworks, Birkinshaw had
produced the first really successful wrought-iron rail, in
1820. These were rolled through a mill to the required shape,
and by this process it was possible to make them much
longer than any rails hitherto used—namely 18 ft. Thus
the number of joints was lessened, indeed Birkinshaw suggested that they might be welded together on the track up
to any length to obviate the jar and noise of passing over the
joints. The idea of welding rails together into long continuous lengths was not followed up until about a hundred
years later. The factor of expansion of the iron due to
variations in temperature had to be taken into account and
a gap left at the rail ends to provide for this. It was only
when the practice of ballasting had developed to such an
extent as to preclude the chance of the rails buckling that
any attempt at long continuous rails was made. This took
place on various railroads in America in the nineteen-
thirties, when rails were welded together up to a length of
2 miles. It has, however, never become a regular practice.
Be that as it may, to Birkinshaw and the craftsmen of the
Bedlington Ironworks belongs the honour of producing the
first wrought-iron rails of any length. On the Stockton and
Darlington Railway they were laid on large foundation
blocks. On the inland stretches of the line, within easy
reach of the limestone quarries stone blocks were used,
while nearer Stockton the blocks were of oak, brought in
by sea.

9 Charleston Viaduct, Manchester and Leeds Railway, where the River Calder and the Rochdale Canal are crossed near Todmorden

From a lithograph by F. Tait, 1845

10   Robert Stephenson

From a photograph taken late in life

The line as originally constructed had only a single track, and was 25½ miles long. The inland terminus took the form of connections to collieries at Etherley and Witton Park. These were rather awkwardly situated so far as transport to Stockton was concerned, as they lay in the valley of the Wear. While nothing could have been further from the minds of the Darlington business men who promoted the railway it might have been more logical to have taken it down the valley of the Wear, and shipped the coals from Sunderland! As it was, although Etherley Colliery lay some 470 ft. above sea level, the line had to ascend the ridge to an altitude of 646 ft., passing to the south-west of Bishop Auckland before descending abruptly towards Shildon. There were four roped-worked inclines, over Etherley Ridge and Brusselton Hill; the trains had to be hauled up one steep slope, eased down the far side, and the process repeated over the second ridge. All this took place in the first 5 miles. For the remaining 20-odd miles the line was level enough for horses or locomotives to be used throughout. There were passing places at intervals, though as the traffic grew one wonders how matters of priority were regulated, and what happened when two lengthy trains, one loaded and one empty approached one another in the middle of a stretch of single line. When the railway was first opened almost complete reliance was placed upon horses for haulage, not only for coal but for all passenger services run between Darlington and Stockton.

Towards the end of the constructional period, George Stephenson, with his son Robert, and John Dixon, made an inspection of the whole line. Afterwards they dined at one of the inns in Stockton, and Stephenson broke his frugal habits by ordering a bottle of wine; it was a very special occasion, and the three of them drank to the success of the railway. It was not in his way to be ostentatious, but on this particular evening he seems to have opened his heart to the two young men who had shared this pioneer task with him, and who were to carry his ideas so very much further. According to John Dixon he said that night:

Now lads, I venture to tell you that I think you will live to see the day when railways will supersede almost all other

4

methods of conveyance in this country—when mail coaches will go by railway, and railroads will become the great highway for the King and all his subjects. The time is coming when it will be cheaper for a working man to travel upon a railway than to walk on foot. I know there are great and almost insurmountable difficulties to be encountered; but what I have said will come to pass as sure as you live. I only wish that I may live to see the day, though that I can scarcely hope for, as I know how slow all human progress is, and with what difficulty I have been able to get the locomotive thus far adopted, notwithstanding my more than ten years' successful experiment at Killingworth.

At the time of opening the line, on September 27th, 1825, the company possessed only one steam locomotive, No. 1 *Locomotion*. This could be described as of the general "Killingworth" type; but the new railway had created intense local interest in the district, and at the formal opening crowds flocked to the lineside to see the "travelling engine". Many were just curious, some sceptical, some violently antagonistic, and had come with pleasurable anticipation of seeing the engine blow up. After a demonstration of working on the Brusselton Incline a train of 38 vehicles was made up to be hauled by *Locomotion*. George Stephenson himself was the driver, with his brother James, and another member of the family on the "footplate" with him. The running of this first train also brings into the picture a man who was to figure considerably in the development of the locomotive—Timothy Hackworth—who on this occasion acted as guard. Even before the start the crowd had a thrill. The engine began to blow off steam! A local newspaper reporter told of the incident thus:

The locomotive, or steam horse, as it was more generally termed, gave a "note of preparation" by some heavy respirations, which seemed to excite alarm among the "Johnny Raws" who had been led by curiosity to the post, and who, when a portion of the steam was let off, fled in affright, accompanied by the old women and young children who surrounded them, under the idea, we suppose, that some horrible explosion was about to take place. They afterwards, however, found courage to return, but to fly again when the safety valve was opened.

So they set off, with a man on horseback riding ahead of the locomotive and carrying aloft a large red flag. People ran alongside in the hope of keeping up with the train; ladies on horseback galloped across the adjoining fields, riding a kind of steeplechase against the engine, and by the time Stockton was reached there were fully 600 people on board, riding, hanging-on, or scrambling over the coals in the excitement of the day. Quite early in the run the man with the flag was warned to get out of the way, for George Stephenson wanted to "open out" the engine; when he did so *Locomotion* with its train of 80 or 90 tons reached the unprecedented speed of 15 m.p.h. It was a gala day indeed, suitably ended by a grand dinner in the Town Hall at Stockton.

That dinner, and the toast list that followed it, brings us forward to a still more momentous point in the development of railways. The thirteenth toast out of twenty-three was: "Success to the projected Liverpool and Manchester Railway". That toast must have struck a pang in Stephenson's heart, for earlier in that year he had lost a vital round in a struggle that might make or end his career. In touching upon the events that led finally to the building, anyone searching among reminiscences, biographies, reports, and so on, becomes increasingly aware of a very tangled skein, and in attempting to give honour where honour is due one may be guilty of over-simplifying the issues. Apart from the business men who backed the enterprise, some of whom came to be numbered among the first directors of the company, four engineering personalities were mainly involved: William James, George Stephenson, John Rennie, the younger, and Charles Vignoles. Towards the end of the nineteenth century a good deal of controversy raged over the question of who was most entitled to be called "The Father of Railways". In perspective such an argument may appear as a waste of words; but the controversy had one lasting value in that it brought to the fore the extraordinary personality and enterprise of William James in the years leading up to 1823–1825. This remarkable man, born at Henley-in-Arden, Warwickshire, in 1771, was at an early age appointed agent to the Earl of Warwick, and receiver to his estate. From this beginning he worked up

an enormous business as land agent and surveyor, and he
has been mentioned already as trying to promote railways
on a vast scale even in the first decade of the nineteenth
century. He had something of the younger Brunel's capacity
for visualising developments on a colossal scale, and in 1815
he went so far as to write to the Prince Regent a long
exposition of the advantages to be derived from steam
locomotion. Whether he received any Royal comment, or
encouragement I cannot say; but James, to the apparent
disregard of his normal business, threw himself with the
utmost zeal into the self-appointed task of promoting railways. There is no doubt that he spent a great deal of his
private fortune. And so eventually he became associated
with the project of a railway between Liverpool and
Manchester.

Enthusiastic as ever, he called upon Mr. Joseph Sandars,
a prominent Liverpool business man, who was then the
moving spirit in the enterprise, and offered his services as
surveyor. His offer was not merely accepted, but through
the financial backing he could give he very soon found himself as the leading promoter, and a first survey of the proposed
line took place in 1822.

The inception of the Liverpool and Manchester Railway
was fraught with quite exceptional difficulties. Opposition
was not confined to the great landed proprietors, or to the
Bridgwater Canal interests, which later, of course, stood to
lose most by the construction of the proposed railway. The
local inhabitants *en masse* seemed to have the most violent
prejudices against the project. Whereas in surveying the
Stockton and Darlington Railway Stephenson met with
nothing but kindness and hospitality from the country folk,
James and his surveying parties often went in danger of
their lives. Samuel Smiles has described the situation
graphically:

> The farmers stationed men at the field-gates with pitch
> forks, and sometimes with guns, to drive them back. At St.
> Helens, one of the chain men was laid hold of by a mob of
> colliers, and threatened to be hurled down a coal pit. A number
> of men, women and children collected and ran after the
> surveyors wherever they made their appearance, bawling

nick-names and throwing stones at them. As one of the chain men was climbing over a gate one day, a labourer made at him with a pitchfork, and ran it through his clothes and into his back; other watchers running up, the chainman who was more stunned than hurt, took to his heels and fled. But that mysterious instrument—the theodolite—most excited the fury of the natives, who concentrated on the man who carried it their fiercest execrations and most offensive nicknames.

A powerful fellow, a noted bruiser, was hired by the surveyor to carry the instrument, with a view to its protection against all assailants; but one day an equally powerful fellow, a St. Helens collier, cock of the walk in the neighbourhood made up to the theodolite bearer to wrest it from him by sheer force. A battle took place, the collier was soundly pummelled, but the natives poured in volleys of stones upon the surveyors and their instruments, and the theodolite was smashed to pieces.

It is small wonder that in such conditions there were errors in the surveys. It says something for James's enthusiasm that he was able to complete the survey at all, even in outline, but it was at this stage, with steam locomotion in view, that James journeyed first to Killingworth and saw Stephenson's locomotives at work. He wrote afterwards to Losh: "It is the greatest wonder of the age, and the forerunner, as I firmly believe, of the most important changes in the internal communications of the kingdom." Despite all his exertions and enthusiasm he and his assistants were not able to submit plans and estimates for the 1822–3 session of Parliament, and this delay—difficult as it would have been to avoid—was fatal to James. About this time a succession of serious financial troubles beset him, so much so that he was declared bankrupt. Illness beset him as well as debt, and he was no longer able to carry out the work of the "Railroad Committee". Thus, the man who had looked so far ahead, and had devoted so much time, energy, and wealth to railway propaganda, as we should call it today, had to drop out of the picture just at the moment when his prophecies and advocacy were about to bear fruit. There is no doubt that James was bitterly resentful of Stephenson's prowess and one of his descendants goes so far as to suggest that it was due to his friendship with Edward Pease that Stephenson was appointed engineer to the Stockton and

4*

Darlington railway. One hesitates to form too sweeping a judgment of his case, but like many another visionary he seems to have lacked just the stability that was the very cornerstone of Stephenson's success.

When it became clear that James could no longer continue, Sandars travelled to Killingworth himself and saw George Stephenson, who was then engaged on the construction of the Stockton and Darlington Railway. The Liverpool and Manchester Railroad Committee needed an engineer to continue their work, and as a result of that visit Stephenson was appointed. The Committee on reconsidering the route proposed by James thought that some alterations were desirable to pass further from the lands of certain noblemen who were known to be antagonistic, and in carrying out the further surveying that was required Stephenson was no more fortunate than James in the attitude of the local populace. In one place he was driven off the ground by keepers, who threatened to duck him in the pond if he was found there again. Gamekeepers were on the look-out by day and night, so that at first Stephenson's idea of surveying by moonlight was of no avail. But in one important sector where a survey had hitherto been impossible his sense of cunning and humour prevailed. A number of men were hired for the occasion, and on a moonlight night they were sent as a decoy, in a direction some distance from the vital spot. At a pre-arranged time they fired off guns in the night, and, as Stephenson hoped, they drew all the gamekeepers in the neighbourhood rapidly in the direction of the noise. While the hue and cry was in progress the surveying party went in and secured the information they wanted.

The extent of opposition in Lancashire perplexed Stephenson. The benefits to be derived from the railway in a rising industrial region were to him so obvious as to need little advocacy. He could understand the opposition of the Bridgwater Canal proprietors and the local landlords; but why the ordinary working men and women? For a period fully one hundred years before the time of broadcasting by radio, the propaganda of the opposition had evidently been most successful. Quoting Smiles again:

The public were appealed to on the subject, pamphlets were written and newspapers were hired to revile the railway. It was declared that its formation would prevent cows grazing and hens laying. The poisoned air from the locomotives would kill birds as they flew over them, and render the preservation of pheasants and foxes no longer possible. Householders were told that their houses would be burnt up by the fire thrown from the engine chimneys; while the air around would be polluted by clouds of smoke. There would no longer be any use for horses; and if railways were extended the species would become extinguished, and oats and hay be rendered unsaleable commodities. Travelling by rail would be highly dangerous and country inns would be ruined. Boilers would burst and blow passengers to atoms. But there was always this consolation to wind up with—that the weight of the locomotive would completely prevent its moving, and that railways, even if made, could never be worked by steam power.

Turning from propaganda to civil engineering, a major point of technical opposition that came very much to the fore when the Bill was in Parliament early in 1825 was the crossing of Chat Moss, an immense peat bog some twelve square miles in extent. At the time the Liverpool and Manchester Railway was projected, nothing more impassable, to the ordinary mind, could have been imagined than this dreary waste; a vast agglomerate of spongy vegetable pulp, the decay of ages! Unlike a normal swamp, which is usually found in a hollow, Chat Moss lay something above the general level of the surrounding country. But it lay also in the direct line between Manchester and Liverpool; William James took his proposed line across it, and Stephenson followed the same route over this section. Both men would, no doubt, have been aware of the important work done shortly before that time in draining the Fens, and the cutting of drains along the course of the railway was to be the prelude to the raising of an embankment. That there were imperfections in the survey there is no doubt, and on certain constructional features of the line Stephenson does not appear to have definite plans when the time came for his cross-examination before the Parliamentary committee; but the opposition made the major part of their case upon the crossing of the Chat Moss, and the extraordinary speed of travel that Stephenson predicted. There were still some people who roundly asserted that locomotives would never move; but the Killingworth and Hetton engines were there for all to see. Their speed, however, was about eight miles per hour. Here on the other hand was George Stephenson proposing to run at twice the speed of a stage coach! "What can be more palpably absurd and ridiculous," commented *The Quarterly Review*.

When discussions were taking place before the presentation of the Bill, with counsel briefed by the promoters, Stephenson told Mr. William Brougham that he expected to get 20 m.p.h. out of his latest locomotives. Counsel retorted that if he did not moderate his views and bring his engines within reasonable speed he would "inevitably damn the whole thing, and be himself regarded as a maniac fit only for Bedlam". When the Bill actually came up in the spring of 1825 Stephenson had an extremely rough passage. In retrospect it would seem that the promoters made an error of judgment in having no qualified engineering opinion to call as witnesses in support of their own proposals, thus taking at least some of the onus from Stephenson. As yet his reputation was merely local. The Stockton and Darlington Railway was not yet in operation, and the attitude of professional engineers in general towards railways was sceptical, where it was not openly hostile. The opponents of the Bill had no difficulty in finding witnesses to put their side of the case. Furthermore, Stephenson was called upon to defend a proposal that was not by any means his own. The route included in the original Bill was, for the most part, that surveyed by William James in 1822, and this included the notorious section across Chat Moss. Whether Stephenson would have gone over the Moss if he himself had started with a clean sheet is a moot point. A diversion two or three miles to the north might have avoided it altogether, but would have taken the line uncomfortably near to the route of the Bridgwater Canal. Stephenson was not one to court difficulties, and in his proposals the railway entered Liverpool from the North, via Bootle, passing to the north of the two great estates of Croxteth and Knowsley and running directly through St. Helens.

When the time came for Stephenson to be cross-examined in the Parliamentary Committee, it seemed fairly evident, from his vagueness on many points connected with the civil engineering work, that he hoped to have a fairly free hand to make such local adjustments as were needed when the line came to be built. That the survey was sketchy in many respects there was no doubts; but unfortunately for him the details of bridges, cuttings, road crossings, and so on, were the very items with which the opposing counsel were familiar from their past experience, and at him they drove, hammer and tongs, hour after hour. From all accounts the courage and adroitness with which he stood up to this gruelling was remarkable, especially as he had the disadvantage of a strong Northumbrian accent, and the difficulty at times of making himself understood. And into the bargain there was the proposed crossing of Chat Moss. Francis Giles, a professional engineer of 22 years standing, spoke thus for the opposition:

> No engineer in his senses would go through Chat Moss if he wanted to make a railroad from Liverpool to Manchester. In my judgment [he went on] a railroad certainly cannot be safely made over Chat Moss without going to the bottom of the Moss. The soil ought all to be taken out, undoubtedly; in doing which, it will not be practicable to approach each end of the cutting, as you make it, with the carriages. No carriages would stand upon the Moss short of the bottom.

So it went on, until the time came for the leading opposition counsel, Mr. Alderson to sum up. In his autobiography written many years later John Rennie has a curious way of tagging adjectives on to personalities when he introduces them to his narrative: "The capable Mr. So and So"; "The energetic Lord Blank"; and so on. One fears that George Stephenson would hardly agree with his reference to "the late able and amiable Baron Alderson"!

In the 1825 Parliamentary Committee Alderson began pleasantly by declaring Stephenson's plan to be

> the most absurd scheme that ever entered into the head of man to conceive. My learned friends almost endeavoured to stop my examination; they wished me to put in the plan, but I had

rather have the exhibition of Mr. Stephenson in that box. I say
he never had a plan—I believe he never had one—I do not
believe he is capable of making one . . .

and so on. There were references to gross ignorance, but
when it came to Chat Moss the "amiable" Mr. Alderson fairly
let himself go. Not only did he deride Stephenson's proposal
for drainage on either side of the line of railway, but he was
inclined to hold up to ridicule even the views of the expert
witnesses on his own side.

> I care not [he threw in] whether Mr. Giles is right or wrong
> in his estimate . . . it is sufficient for me to suggest and to show
> that this scheme of Mr. Stephenson's is impossible, or imprac-
> ticable . . . I have heard of culverts, which have been put upon
> the Moss which, after having been surveyed the day before,
> have the next morning disappeared . . . there is nothing, it
> appears, except long sedgy grass, and a little soil to prevent it
> sinking into the shades of eternal night. I have now done, sir,
> with Chat Moss, and there I leave this railroad.

In the circumstances it was not surprising that the Bill
was thrown out. It was a great disappointment to the
promoters, but most of all to Stephenson, and his mortification was increased doubly by the next step of the Liverpool
and Manchester Railroad Committee. Great faith though
they still had in Stephenson, they could not be otherwise
than aware of his shortcomings as a witness, and his lack
of civil engineering experience on the largest scale. The
next step is best told by Rennie:

> The late Earl of Lonsdale, then Lord Lowther, one of the
> Lords of the Treasury, a very able and intelligent young man,
> knowing me from my connection with London Bridge, and with
> the Whitehaven Harbour, of which I was the engineer (where
> his father was the chief owner of all the great collieries round
> the town), asked my opinion about the proposed new system,
> whether I thought it was likely to succeed. I told him frankly
> that I thought it would. His Lordship replied, "I think so too";
> and he offered me the post of engineer to the Manchester and
> Liverpool Railway, adding, "Although it will be greatly
> opposed I think we shall carry it." I replied that my brother
> and myself would be happy to undertake it, provided that we
> did not interfere with Mr. Stephenson or any other engineer

who had previously been employed. Lord Lonsdale said that he would arrange all that with the Company, and my brother and myself were accordingly appointed engineers-in-chief.

Viscount Lowther, as he was then, had by that time become Chairman of the Committee, and the appointment of the Rennies involved nothing less than the dismissal of Stephenson.

John Rennie and his brother, with projects on hand in many parts of the country, and important European connections as well, could not give detailed personal attention to this important task, and so, in Rennie's own words "we selected the present energetic and talented engineer, Mr. Charles Vignoles, to make the necessary surveys for Parliament". There was all the difference in the world between the bearing and speech of this polished young soldier, and "Geordie the engine-wright", and when the time came for the Bill to be presented again the Rennies let Vignoles bear the brunt of the cross-examination. Chat Moss remained, and John Rennie, wise very many years after the event, refers to the opposition they encountered. "All that was required", he wrote, "was to drain the surface by moderate-sized drains, so as to get rid of the superfluous water, then the foundations for the rails would be sufficiently solid to bear anything." It sounds easy, but did not prove *quite* so easy to accomplish. Nevertheless the experience of the Rennies carried much weight, where Stephenson's word had availed not at all, and the Bill was carried. It was a great personal triumph for Charles Vignoles, though he in turn was soon to suffer mortification over this bitterly contested railway. The principal difference between Stephenson's route and the one for which the Act was obtained lay in the approach to Liverpool. Instead of going through St. Helens the line was carried several miles to the south and approached its western end in almost a straight line. Very heavy cutting work was to be involved at Olive Mount and the final entry to Liverpool was made by a tunnel from Edge Hill.

When the Act for the construction of the line was obtained the Rennies expected to be appointed as engineers. It had been in large measure due to their efforts and their name that the Bill had gone through; but the Executive Committee realised that when it came to the actual building of the line the Rennies, if appointed, could only exercise what might be termed a remote control over the work due to their other multifarious activities. There would have to be a resident engineer. By that time the Stockton and Darlington Railway had been in operation for some months, and despite his failure to convince at the first Parliamentary attempt the Committee still had great faith in Stephenson. It was therefore suggested to John Rennie that Stephenson should be resident engineer. This was a rather unlikely proposition, and may have been made deliberately to force the issue. In any event John Rennie and his brother stood firm. If they were to act as engineers-in-chief they reserved the right to appoint a resident engineer of their own selection—in fact Vignoles had already been sent up to Lancashire in anticipation of the work, and in continuance of his services during the third survey. They were quite content for Stephenson to have the locomotive department as a separate and independent command. At that time the engineering profession as a whole was still by no means convinced that steam locomotion was going to be a success, and one could quite understand that the Rennies would be only too glad to be relieved of any responsibility in that direction. But in any case the Executive Committee refused to accept Rennie's conditions; the brief association of the firm with the Liverpool and Manchester Railway was severed, and George Stephenson was appointed engineer-in-chief.

Charles Vignoles was thereupon left in a very awkward position. While working under the direction of the Rennies he was actually on the railway staff, and now came under George Stephenson. The Rennies apparently had no other appointment to offer him and it was not to be expected that George Stephenson would look very kindly upon one who had recently been on the other side, as it were. There was another point too, Vignoles was originally destined for a military career, and had a somewhat fiery and outspoken manner. From the very outset it was clear that, to use a colloquialism, he did not "get on" with Stephenson. In a letter to a friend written about a year later he says:

I acknowledge having on many occasions differed with him (and that in common with almost all other engineers) because it appeared to me that he did not look on the concern with a liberal and expanded view, but with a microscopic eye; magnifying details, and pursuing a petty system of parsimony, very proper in a private colliery, or in a small undertaking, but wholly inapplicable to this national work.

I also plead guilty of having neglected to court Mr. S's favour by crying down all other engineers, especially those in London, for, though I highly respect his great natural talents, I could not shut my eyes to certain deficiencies.

All these circumstances combined gave rise to a feeling of ill-will on his part towards me, which he displayed on every occasion; particularly where I showed a want of practical knowledge of unimportant minutiae, rendered familiar to him by experience.

It is obvious, of course, that Vignoles was not the kind of man Stephenson himself would have chosen for an assistant, and he probably found the position equally awkward. Then again Stephenson had the task of building, not the line that he himself had surveyed, but the one Vignoles had surveyed for the Rennies. The uneasy and troubled association came to a head over some errors in the survey of the Edge Hill tunnel. Vignoles was inclined to treat them lightly, as things that could have been put right without trouble or expense; but in the strained circumstances that existed it was perhaps only natural that the whole affair became magnified out of its true proportion, and as a result Vignoles resigned. Whatever Stephenson thought of him it was evident that Vignoles stood high in the esteem of the profession itself, for on April 10th, 1827, only a few months after his resignation, he was elected a Member of the Institution of Civil Engineers (62). His name recurs time and again in the early history of railways; but reading his biography it seems all too clear that fortune dealt very severely with a man who had great nobility of character, who weathered the storm of professional disaster that would have broken most men for good and all, and who fought back to achieve in old age the Blue Riband of the profession—the Presidency of the Institution of Civil Engineers. But at the time of his break with Stephenson he was still a spirited young man of 34, and the most serious and troublous part of his life lay ahead. With his going Stephenson was left unfettered by any past associations on the railway. He divided the line into three sections, and appointed as resident engineers three of his own pupils, Joseph Locke, William Allcard, and John Dixon. Locke had the Liverpool end, where there was considerable trouble with the Edge Hill tunnel, and Dixon had to deal with Chat Moss.

If Chat Moss had figured prominently in the Parliamentary Committee stages it was to prove no less a tremendous task in actual construction. One can smile at John Rennie's facile description of how it should be done, for despite all that had been said previously the Moss itself was a somewhat daunting prospect. It was left to Locke to show Dixon what he was in for! Work had actually started, but as the men attempted to cut the drains on either side of the line of the railway the sedge flowed into these drains, and filled them up as fast as they were cut. The line had been staked out, and levels taken with the aid of planks laid on the surface, and along these planks Locke and Dixon made their way. Suddenly Dixon slipped, and in a trice he was up to his knees in the bog; struggling only sent him deeper in, but fortunately some workmen nearby saw his plight and dragged him out— not a very encouraging start! But with Locke's encouragement and reassurance they floundered on and eventually got to the farther end. Dixon, who was devoted to George Stephenson and full of the enthusiasm of youth, was really more perplexed than daunted. At this stage he could not conceive how heavy locomotives and trains could possibly travel over a bog that would not support his own weight. During the survey men had fixed large boards to the soles of their feet, to prevent them sinking, by distributing the weight over a larger area, and Dixon henceforth adopted this idea himself.

How deep down the bog extended nobody seems to have known; but Stephenson's intention was to "float" the road over the unstable portion, building the "formation" on which the rails would be laid on a broad mattress of heather and brushwood laid across the bog. At first a footpath of heather was laid down so that men could walk beside the

line of the railway without any fear of sinking; a temporary
line of light railway was next put down to carry the wagons
needed for conveyance of materials, and the ease with which
the support for this line was made encouraged even the
faintest of hearts. But the encouragement was short-lived.
The drains could not be cut, on account of the quick silting
up that followed, and in the softest parts the mattress of
heather sank under the weight of the railroad itself—let
alone any trains. On stretches like this it was the intention
to run the line roughly at the level of the surface of the bog,
and the places where subsidences occurred were corrected by
packing more heather and more cakes of firm turf under the
track itself. The drains were eventually consolidated by
laying in tar barrels, so soon as the trench had been dug,
eventually forming underground sewers of wood, instead of
brick or iron.

The line over the Moss was four miles long, and at the
Manchester end due to a general depression in the level a
shallow embankment had to be formed. While in general
the principle of the floating mattress was sufficient to carry
the road and the trains it was quite another matter with the
weight of earth required to make an embankment. Men
were employed to cut the driest moss in the neighbourhood,
and this was duly tipped in to make the embankment. But
each load had gradually disappeared beneath the sedgy
surface, and weeks went by with nothing to show for this
work. The local wise-acres began to shake their heads; even
Stephenson's most trusted assistants grew uneasy, and the
directors really grew alarmed. All that had been said in the
Parliamentary contest came back to them, and matters got
to the stage of abandonment. Stephenson alone retained
his full confidence in ultimate success. But it was "touch
and go". A board meeting was held on Chat Moss, when the
question of an alternative route was discussed. Great
though the expense had been so far, a diversion with all
the complications of new surveys, a fresh Bill to be presented
to Parliament, and above all the fulfilment of the direst
prophecies made by their opponents, was unthinkable. And
so the filling went on, for week after week until at last the
embankment began to rise firm and solid. The appearance of

it, when ultimately finished was likened to a long ridge of tightly pressed tobacco leaf. Difficult though the work had been the cost of the four miles of line over the Moss was £28,000, whereas the "expert" Francis Giles, in his evidence for the opposition, gave the probable cost as £270,000!

11   Olive Mount Cutting

The relationship of the engineer - in - chief and his assistants towards the Railway Company came into question during constructional days. George Stephenson regarded Dixon, Locke, and Allcard as his personal assistants to be given assignments at will, whereas some of the Liverpool and Manchester Railway directors felt they should be employed exclusively on the line. This point was quickly cleared to give Stephenson freedom of action, and with railway projects springing up in other directions Locke (18) was released from his duties at the Liverpool end of the line, and sent to make detailed investigations of other lines on which George Stephenson was being consulted. While he was away further errors were discovered in the survey of the Edge Hill tunnel. Locke's successor had drawn attention to these, and that minority of the directors who had always shown signs of opposition to Stephenson were not content with

calling for an independent check of the survey. The resignation of Vignoles over earlier errors at this location were still
fresh in mind, and things were made worse when the Board
invited Joseph Locke to check the survey. Locke had to
agree that errors existed, and there is no doubt that Stephenson took this episode very badly. While he had not been
personally responsible for the survey he had, as engineer-in-
chief, assumed responsibility for it, and while Locke remained
with him for several years after, their relations were henceforth not so cordial as before. There is little doubt that
Stephenson felt Locke should have refused to undertake the
independent check, in view of their previous personal relations; but Locke's star was then very much in the ascendant,
and he was held in high confidence by the Liverpool section
of the Board. He was placed in a very difficult position:
to have refused would have caused great offence in
highly influential quarters; to have accepted would almost
certainly have upset George Stephenson, and he risked the
latter.

Great though the attention centred upon it came to be,
the Liverpool and Manchester did not, after all, prove to be
the second public railway in the world. That honour belongs
to the little Canterbury and Whitstable, which was opened
a few months before the northern line. In the years of
reviving trade, following the post-war slump of 1817–19,
certain prominent citizens of Canterbury sought means to
revive the old prosperity of their city as a seaport by opening
up the long derelict navigation on the River Stour, and so
providing communication by water with Sandwich. Then,
one day in 1823, William James arrived in the city on one
of his free-lance railway prospecting journeys and suggested
a railway, not to Sandwich but to Whitstable, which was
only six miles distant. He met one or two influential persons,
but before anything of a company had been formed, James
set off in his usual exuberant style and made a survey on
his own account. But when the railway came to be seriously
considered it was decided to consult George Stephenson; he
deputed the work of a detailed survey to John Dixon and
plans were duly lodged with Parliament for the session of
1825. The route was direct enough, but very hilly, and it

included the first railway tunnel in the world to be brought into regular service.

There is a picturesque story about this tunnel which has been quoted by various writers. When the survey was first made so the story goes, the directors were disappointed to find that no tunnel was included on the route. In the idiom popularised by that modern character Mr. Chad it was a case of "What, no tunnel?" Following which came the plea, "Oh but we *must* have a tunnel." And the story goes on to say how the engineer was instructed to alter the survey so that a tunnel could be included on the route. Actually, of course, this story is something of a fairy tale. The line was laid out in a similar way to the colliery lines of the north, using steep gradients and cable haulage where necessary, and the tunnel at Tyler's Hill was a natural feature of the direct line. The only other railway tunnel then projected was that on the Liverpool and Manchester at Edge Hill, and it is hardly likely that such a feature would have been insisted upon just for novelty's sake. When the Bill was passed in June 1825, and the time came for the construction to start, Stephenson was appointed engineer, and he deputed Joseph Locke to carry out the work for him—in the early stages at any rate. No particular difficulties appear to have occurred in the building of the line. From a letter written in January 1826 it is evident that William James at one time hoped to have some association with the work, as he writes:

I have not heard from Canterbury, therefore I conclude Stephenson's intrigues still are predominant there; in short, it is quite indispensible that I should take up some pursuit in which I can have some compensation for my labour, and I shall make land-agency and other objects my principal pursuits in future.

The case of James was a very sad one. One can imagine his eagerness to promote railways, his enthusiasm and drive, and then when things worked up to a climax he was baulked every time.

The Canterbury and Whitstable Railway is important from the locomotive point of view, not so much in respect of the one engine it originally possessed, but in the personality of the one man who drove it. The subject of locomotive development is dealt with as a separate story in the third chapter of this book, but at this stage it should be mentioned that by then the firm of Robert Stephenson and Company had been formed, with George Stephenson, Nicholas Wood, and Richardson, as the moving spirits. Stephenson intended that his son should look after the locomotive building interests of the family, and the new firm was formed under Robert's name. They built locomotives for the Stockton and Darlington Railway, and the Canterbury and Whitstable *Invicta* came from the same works. With Stephenson in the Newcastle works was a young mechanic named Edward Fletcher; he assisted in the trials of several new locomotives, and he was selected to take the *Invicta* to Canterbury. She was shipped by sea from Newcastle and was landed at Whitstable, and in the early days of the line she was driven by Edward Fletcher. A remarkable link of continuity is provided by this incident, for some 25 years later after an unbroken experience in the building and running of locomotives Fletcher was appointed locomotive superintendent of the North Eastern Railway, with his headquarters at Gateshead; he continued in office until 1883, and his latest engines continued in regular passenger service long enough for me to photograph one at the Western end of the old Stockton and Darlington line in 1923.

Robert Stephenson deputised for his father at the ceremonial opening of the Canterbury and Whitstable Railway; but concerning his presence the *Kent Herald* says:

On the removal of the cloth the usual loyal toasts were given, after which followed the healths of several gentlemen connected with the railway. On the health of Mr. Robert Stephenson, Civil Engineer, being given, that gentleman acknowledged the compliment, but spoke so low that we could not hear distinctly what he said . . .

Speech-maker or not, Robert Stephenson was rapidly coming into the picture.

Despite the successful working of Stephenson's engines on the colliery lines in Northumberland and Durham there was a time in the late eighteen-twenties when the whole future of the steam locomotive hung in the balance. Many among the most progressive business men of the day were quite unconvinced of the need for increased speed of conveyance for merchandise and minerals. The professional·engineers stood aloof, as much from their jealousy and antagonism to Stephenson as from scepticism of the outcome. There were certainly solid grounds for scepticism. Once the Stockton and Darlington Railway was opened for traffic Stephenson's widening interests took him frequently away from the district; his son was abroad, and the onus, at a very difficult time, fell upon the Locomotive Superintendent, Timothy Hackworth. The length of run was much longer than anything previously needed on the Killingworth and Hetton railways; the engines frequently ran short of steam, and on the adverse gradients they stalled even in favourable weather conditions. Theodore West, in one of his quaint little monographs tells how the driver would call out to his fireman:

> "Give it to her, Bill, mon, give it to her," as Bill, with his shovel, strode alongside frantically scraping up small ballast and dashing it before the wheels in place of sand to make them bite (sand boxes were not then invented)—but in vain—puff! p-u-f-f-f! Engine and wagons at length stood still. Thereupon ensued a passionate rousing up of the fire, a brief and rather heavy swearing match at engines generally and this one in particular, then, hot and tired, the two men would sit down on the near railings or bank for a quiet pipe, while steam slowly rose to going pitch, then once more they mounted and went.

There were mechanical troubles too; wheels came loose on the axles, a wheel broke altogether, and the newer engines from Stephenson's works in Newcastle were no better. One finds Edward Pease writing to Robert Stephenson in America, thus:

> I can assure thee that thy business at Newcastle, as well as thy father's engineering, have suffered very much from thy absence, and unless thou soon return the former will be given up, as Mr. Longridge is not able to give it that attention it requires, and what is done is not done with credit to the house.

But Robert Stephenson was not able to return at once, and it was probably for the very practical reason that George

Stephenson could not afford to buy him out that Pease remained in the firm. The whole situation was on a razor-edge. To handle the coal traffic the Stockton and Darlington Railway had to employ more horses, and by the end of 1826 Stephenson was so thoroughly involved with the Liverpool and Manchester Railroad that he could do little more than to send suggestions and encouragement to Hackworth by letter. It was at this juncture that Timothy Hackworth made his notable contribution to the development of the steam locomotive, by building the *Royal George* engine at Shildon works. It is sometimes said that this famous engine was no more than a rebuild of an older one, as certain parts recovered were utilised to save expense; but in its conception and design the *Royal George* was a new engine.

Hackworth had then had as much practical experience as anyone living in the maintenance and running of steam loco-motives, and the features he included in the *Royal George* were the direct result of that experience. The engine was much larger and heavier than any of the Stephenson-built examples; it had six-wheels coupled, and a very much larger boiler. I must not digress at this stage upon the mechanical details of this engine save to remark that it had tenders at both ends. The fire door was at the front end, beside the chimney; so that the fireman rode on the leading tender, while the driver rode on the trailing one. The *Royal George* worked successfully and its introduction just about saved the situation on the Stockton and Darlington Railway. Even so the outlook elsewhere was pretty bleak, and for a time it seemed that Stephenson stood alone in his championship of steam locomotion. Some of his staunchest friends among the business community were not merely alarmed at the speeds he so confidently predicted, but doubtful of success at all. To him, railways without steam haulage were hardly worth while, and yet even after he had been appointed engineer-in-chief of the Liverpool and Manchester, the ques-tion of motive power remained unsettled for a long time. Many board meetings on the subject were held; some of the directors still pinned their faith in horses; and a delegation went on a tour of railways in Northumberland and Durham, in 1828, to study the working methods. Concerning this

visit Timothy Hackworth got his instructions from Edward
Pease thus:

> Esteemed Friend,
>
> I am informed that a deputation is coming from Liverpool
> to see our way, but more particularly to make enquiry about
> Locomotive power. Have the engines and men as neat and
> clean as can be, and be ready with thy calculations, not only
> showing the saving, but how much more work they do in a
> given time. Have no doubt will do thy best to have all sided
> and in order in thy department.
>
> Thy frd.
Edward Pease

With the deputation came Joseph Locke and Robert
Stephenson, who by that time had returned from America.
This visit was fortunately conclusive in one respect, for in
view of the traffic expected to develop on the Liverpool and
Manchester Railway, and in view of the delays the delegation
witnessed with horse-haulage on the colliery lines, they came
back convinced that horses were unsuitable.

Even so some of the directors had second thoughts on
this particular point when the Newcastle and Carlisle Railway Bill was passed in 1829, on the express condition that
locomotives should *not* be used. All this was completely out
of tune with Stephenson's whole conception of railways—
unless speed of transit was assured the lines would not be
able to carry the traffic offered. Yet among others, few had
any faith in the future of the locomotive. One cannot help
feeling that the way in which the leading engineers of the
day hung back influenced the minds of many men. If great
and unquestioned authorities, such as Telford and John
Rennie, had come forward boldly in favour of steam locomotion the tide would quickly have turned; but on the other
hand one can appreciate their reluctance to espouse a development which Stephenson, a self-taught and still obscure
mechanic, had made particularly his own. The attitude of
the established professionals was one of carefully veiled
hostility. The indecision of the Liverpool and Manchester
board led to their being inundated with all sorts of wild-cat
schemes of propulsion: water power, carbonic acid gas, and

even hydrogen were suggested, while stationary steam engines and cable-haulage featured in many proposals submitted. All this merely confused the issue. In the light of these alternatives, the directors consulted their own engineer, only to receive a solid reiteration of his unshaken faith in steam locomotives as the sole means of power. The result of course was deadlock, and to solve it the board decided to call in two professional engineers of high reputation to examine the system of fixed-engine haulage, which was favoured by a majority of the directors, and the alternative of travelling steam locomotives advocated by Stephenson.

The recommendation of Messrs. J. Walker and J. U. Rastrick, following visits to Stephenson's lines in Northumberland and Durham, and to others, were surprising to say the least of them. They seem to have looked at the question purely from that of working expenses. One item was the cost of moving a ton of goods 30 miles—6·4 pence by fixed engines, and 8·36 pence by locomotive. Again there is no reference to speed, and one can imagine that the thoughts of George Stephenson must have been bordering upon despair when these two distinguished gentlemen solemnly proposed dividing the line between Liverpool and Manchester into nineteen stages of about 1½ miles each, with twenty-one stationary engines at the intermediate points. The cumbersome nature of such methods does not bear thinking about, and yet for a time George Stephenson was fighting practically a lone battle. But he never gave up. He continually urged his views upon the directors. That he discussed things very earnestly with his immediate assistants is clear from a pamphlet published in 1830 by Robert Stephenson and Joseph Locke: "Observations on the Comparative Merits of Locomotives and Fixed Engines". This pamphlet was a summary of the arguments that George Stephenson put to the Board, and which had no doubt been hammered out between the three engineers. One gathers that Robert Stephenson had a big share in the framing of these arguments. He was frequently in correspondence with Hackworth and the latter was staunchness itself in his loyalty to steam locomotion.

Stationary engines [he wrote to Robert Stephenson] are by no means adapted to the public line of railway. I take no account here of a great waste of capital. But you will fail in proving to the satisfaction of anyone not conversant with this subject the inexpediency of such a system. . . .

I hear the Liverpool Company have concluded to use fixed engines. Some will look on with surprise; but as you can well afford it, it is all for the good of the science and of the trade to try both plans. Do not discompose yourself, my dear Sir; if you express your manly, firm, decided opinion, you have done your part as their adviser. And if it happens to be read some day in the newspapers—"Whereas the Liverpool and Manchester Railway has been strangled with ropes" we shall not accuse you of guilt in being accessory either before or after the fact!

The case was admirably summed up in the Stephenson and Locke report thus:

That in considering the long chain of connected power of the stationary engines, given out by so many machines, with the continual crossings of the trains from one line to the other, and subject to the Government of no fewer than 150 men, whose *individual* attention is *all* requisite to preserve the communication between two of the most important towns in the kingdom. We cannot but express our decided conviction, that a system that necessarily involves, by a single accident, the stoppages of the whole, is totally unfitted for a public railway.

In any case, by sheer persistence George Stephenson managed to stave off the proposal to instal fixed engines, and so at length the directors agreed to offer a prize of £500 for the best locomotive that should fulfil certain stipulated conditions. The result was the ever-memorable trial at Rainhill in October 1829. The construction of the *Rocket*, and the development that flowed from it, are described in a later chapter; but the astonishing performance put up on October 8th proved the great turning point in railway history. There were no longer any doubts about steam locomotives; it was now an unquestioned success. The engine worked throughout with consistent reliability, and at one point reached the extraordinary speed for those days of 29 m.p.h.

How the Liverpool and Manchester Railway was completed and brought into service is told in the chapter dealing

12   Sonning Cutting, near Reading (G.W.R.): a timber trestle bridge
carrying the road over the railway

From a drawing by J. C. Bourne, 1846

13   Iron bridge over the Trent, built by Vignoles on the
Midland Counties Railway, 1839

From a lithograph by G. Hawkins, Junr.

14   Bathford Bridge, G.W.R.

From a drawing by E. A. Tackle

15   Blasting the rocks near Leighton Buzzard
Both from drawings by J. C. Bourne, 1837

16   Building the Wolverton Embankment
Robert Stephenson, engineer

BUILDING THE LONDON AND BIRMINGHAM LINE

specifically with locomotives; but its success gave encouragement to all who were feeling their way towards railway
promotion, though there were still many who were exceedingly hostile and sceptical. In the eighteen-thirties a group
of important new lines were sanctioned by Parliament, as
follows:

1833   The London and Birmingham
1833   The Grand Junction
1834   The London and Southampton
1835   The Great Western
1836   The Birmingham and Derby
1836   The North Midland

With the exception of the Great Western, all these were
built by engineers of the Stephenson "school". George himself began the Grand Junction, and did the Birmingham and
Derby, and the North Midland; Robert Stephenson did the
London and Birmingham, and Locke, the Southampton.
Before its completion Locke also became engineer of the
Grand Junction, and so commenced that long association
with the West Coast Route to Scotland that resulted in his
building practically the whole line from Lancaster to Carlisle,
and onwards to Perth and Aberdeen. George Stephenson's
pupils were all-rounders; both his son and Locke were more
than ordinarily interested and expert in locomotive construction, and while Robert Stephenson's interest was turned
to the development of the locomotive building industry,
Locke's interest was turned to the improvement of engine
performance on the railways with which he was directly
connected—notably the Grand Junction and the Caledonian
group. On special occasions Locke and Robert Stephenson
themselves drove important trains. One of the last recorded
occasions was that of a special for King Louis Philippe, of
France, from Farnborough to Gosport, on the Southampton
line. Then when the weather proved so bad that the King
wouldn't risk the crossing to Treport, but asked for arrangements to be made for him to cross from Dover to Calais,
Joseph Locke again drove the Royal Train, this time back to
the Nine Elms terminus.

Railways were now being constructed on a greater scale

5

than ever before. The London and Birmingham was 112 miles long; the Southampton was nearly 80 miles, and the North Midland 72 miles. Construction work had to be organised on a vast scale, and in the carrying through of such projects the contractor comes to the fore. In the earliest days of railways there were plenty of men who were fitted by status and experience to do relatively small and simple civil engineering jobs; but works such as the London and Birmingham called for a resource and organising ability on a scale never yet seen—one might almost say since the building of the great Pyramid! While the railway company's engineer, Stephenson, Locke, or whoever he might have been, took the ultimate responsibility the work was contracted out, often section by section. The letting of such contracts sometimes called for a clear judgment, of character as much as engineering; for in those days many men were undertaking work of a novel kind, and there was usually no previous achievement by which a prospective contractor's suitability could be assessed. In the building of the early railways one name stands out— that of Thomas Brassey (19). He deserves indeed, to rank among the great men who made possible railways on the grand scale. He has been dubbed "The Navvy King", yet anyone less like the swashbuckling, son-of-a-gun type of overseer would be hard to imagine.

Thomas Brassey was descended from a very old English family who had been landed proprietors on a modest scale in Cheshire. No very great wealth was attached to the in- herence, but its longevity had bred that innate culture and quality that belonged to a country gentleman of the old school. At the age of sixteen young Brassey was articled to a land surveyor and agent in Chester, and in these early years he assisted in making some of the surveys for the Holyhead road, of which Telford was the engineer. As land agent he quickly showed he had keen business acumen, and when out of his articles he was soon made a partner. His activities extended, and so it came that he undertook the management of a stone quarry at Stourton. This enterprise was fortuitous beyond measure, for it so happened that the Liverpool and Manchester Railway was then under construc- tion, and stone was wanted for the Sankey Viaduct. George

17 The Sankey Viaduct

Stephenson went to the Stourton quarry, met Thomas Brassey, and a contract was made for stone; but Stephenson, who had a rare gift for picking his men, took an immediate liking for the young agent, and induced him to co-operate in the task of building railways. His first railway contract was for the building of the Penkridge Viaduct, between Wolverhampton and Stafford on the Grand Junction in 1834.

It was a small beginning, but in its execution Brassey displayed as much ability in the organisation of the labour force as he did in the faultless execution of the work. As the opportunities came to extend his activities Brassey showed a talent for administration. In his early years he made himself a master of all the detail of railway construction; later, by the skilful choosing of sub-contractors, and no less by the choice of his own assistants he was able to handle with equal facility a dozen or more large railway contracts, in England, Scotland, France and Spain simultaneously! But this is anticipating, for it was in the earlier English main lines that the technique of construction was worked out. When the Liverpool and Manchester, the Grand Junction, and others were built the excavating of cuttings had to be done by hand (12, 23). Transport of the earth cut out was by horse and wheelbarrow, and where rock formations were encountered all the "spoil" had again to be carted away by the same primitive means. The most clear-cut organisation of the labour force was called for, if a great deal of time and effort was not to be wasted. George Stephenson himself did a good deal of pioneer work in this respect on the Liverpool and Manchester Railway; but despite Chat Moss and Olive Mount Cutting the works there were on a limited scale to those which were tackled later.

When the Grand Junction Railway Act was obtained George Stephenson was appointed as engineer-in-chief, but a dispute soon arose as to the organisation of the constructional work. Stephenson wanted to carry on as he had done on the Liverpool and Manchester, with three resident engineers; but the Board wanted a single resident, to have full responsibility for the whole line in Stephenson's absence. Locke, of course, was the man they had in mind, but in the face of Stephenson's opposition they made a very uneasy compromise: that there should be two resident engineers— Locke, taking the northern end—but in Stephenson's absence Locke should assume responsibility for the whole. This was not calculated to improve relations between the two men! Further trouble arose over the method of allocating contracts. Locke favoured the issuing of precise specifications for the way the work should be done, while Stephenson preferred a rather more "free and easy" method. The directors were naturally interested in the progress of the work and were so impressed by Locke's methods as to give instructions for them to be used throughout the line; this again put Stephenson in an awkward position.

Good practical man though he was, the handling of a mass of figures and calculations was not his strong point, and when his chosen assistant at the Birmingham end of the line also proved unequal to the task, a very unfortunate comparison between progress on the northern and southern divisions

gradually became apparent: while Locke excelled, his opposite
number was in a state of complete muddle. The directors
could hardly allow such a situation to continue, and they
appointed Locke to act as joint chief engineer, with particular
responsibility for issuing the specifications and getting the
contracts placed. In other circumstances this dual responsibility might have worked, but in view of the grievance
Stephenson had nursed towards Locke since the days of the
Edge Hill tunnel, it was impracticable on the Grand Junction,
and after a very short time George Stephenson resigned.
Unhappily the estrangement between the two men was
almost complete, though fortunately Robert Stephenson and
Locke remained the closest of friends for the rest of their
lives.

It was on the Grand Junction that the great association
between Locke and Brassey began. Locke was indefatigable.
Assistant engineers and contractors complained that he
walked them off their legs. He thought nothing of walking
right through from Warrington to Birmingham in three
days—inspecting all the works as he went. But in Thomas
Brassey he met his match; here was a man whose energy was
equal to his own, and it was not surprising that the association
proved so fruitful as to take the two men, as engineer and
contractor, into many lands. Under Brassey's supervision
the gangs of labourers were carefully organised so that the
dug-out earth or stone was cleared in a series of well-defined
routes. The wheelbarrow runs did not interfere with the men
engaged on the digging. One of Mr. Brassey's time-keepers
has described such a scene: "I think as fine a spectacle as any
man could witness, who is accustomed to look at work, is to
see a cutting in full operation, with about twenty wagons
being filled, every man at his post, and every man with his
shirt open, working in the heat of the day, the gangers
looking about and everything going like clockwork." The
contractors who built railways in England were fortunate in
that a certain amount of first class labour was ready to hand.
Many men had been employed in the making of embankments and cuttings for canals, and men of this type, with a
good deal of rough experience in earthworks, formed the
backbone of the contractors' forces. In their earlier works

they were known as navigators, which name soon became
abbreviated to "navvy". The work they did each day was
prodigious, and it is recorded that in Brassey's day there
were no trade unions amongst them, and very few strikes.

The Rev. W. E. Dickson, through whose parish one of the
early railways was constructed wrote, in 1854:

> As in the affairs of the political world situations of great
> difficulty and crisis invariably call forth men competent to deal
> with them, so the necessity for human labour of unexampled
> extent, created by the projection of these great works, seems to
> have called into existence a race of men specially adapted for
> the occasion. The ploughman, or thresher, who plods through
> his day's work at the farm would be amazed to see the rapid
> movements and prodigious energy of these men. A careless and
> thoughtless race they are, resembling much the sailor in char-
> acter: highly paid for their herculean labours, they spend their
> few hours of leisure in recruiting their strength for the next
> effort by feasts of the most substantial kind, in which even
> expensive luxuries are not forgotten—young ducks, and green
> peas, for instance, at a period of the year when such delicacies
> command high prices.

When Brassey undertook railway contracts abroad he
usually took with him a number of English navvies to form
the spearhead of his labour force, and these great fellows
seemed to delight in showing how much more they could do
in a day than the French and Italian labourers. "Mon Dieu!
Les Anglais, comme ils travaillent!" exclaimed a gentleman
of the neighbourhood as he watched work in progress on the
Paris and Rouen line. Some present-day writers have tended
to paint a rather lurid picture of conditions during the
building of the early railways, with drunkenness, brawling,
and, generally prevailing, an atmosphere of middle-west
lawlessness in the "gold rush" days. The English navvy was
certainly a pretty tough chap, but again one turns to the
contemporary writing of Mr. Dickson. He found in all those
with whom he talked an honest bluntness and hearty good-
will. Several poor fellows, victims of accidents that occasionally took place, he attended on their death-beds, and there
is no doubt that he grew to like the navvies as a race and
found the construction of the line through his parish an

enrichment of his experience of human character. This particular job formed one of Brassey's contracts, and in talking to the men he found that many of them had been in his service for many years, both in England and abroad.

Brassey had the rare quality of personal magnetism. In his earlier days he knew many of the navvies by name, and always had a friendly greeting for them as he walked around on inspections. It was no doubt this character that enabled him to build up a great organisation of loyal assistants. He was no more than twenty-nine years of age when he took the contract for the Penkridge Viaduct, but even then his organising ability was evident, and caught the eye of Joseph Locke. A railway engineer is naturally attracted towards a contractor who gives him a thoroughly sound job, and can be relied upon to honour all his agreements both in price and date for completion of the work. Brassey, it was said, was a deeply religious man, and regarded his contracts with the utmost solemnity. Perhaps the most striking instance of this occurred in France, when he was building the Paris–Rouen line. In the course of the work the Barentin Viaduct collapsed. It was a huge structure, 100 ft. high and more than a quarter of a mile long, and the reasons for its fall were, to say the least of it, complicated. But with Brassey and his partner there was no waiting to argue the reasons or the responsibility; the line was urgently needed, and his one aim was to rebuild as quickly as possible, regardless of everything else, and settle the "paper-work" afterwards.

Speed, combined with first class work, was always the essence of the contract where Thomas Brassey was concerned, and as the works grew in magnitude, so methods were improved in proportion. In laying out a line of railway it was always the aim of the engineer to make the amount of excavation from cuttings roughly balance the material needed for embankments, and in hilly country an embankment would often immediately succeed a cutting (9). Brassey's men soon found that wheelbarrows were not quick enough. Temporary narrow gauge railways were laid down, and large wagons were brought up for carrying the earth. The railways were carried from the neighbouring cutting, where excavation was in progress to the furthest extent of an embankment;

the wagons were conveyed in a train to within measurable distance of the tip, and then a daring and dangerous procedure was in regular use. At the edge of the tip a sleeper was placed across the rails; the wagons were detached and one by one, each was drawn forward by the horse at a brisk speed. Nearing the edge of the tip the wagon was uncoupled, the horse stepped nimbly aside, and the wheels of the wagon struck the sleeper lying athwart the rails, and the wagon overturned sending its contents down the slope.

But Brassey was not available everywhere, and on some of the early railways difficulties arose through the experience or incompetence of the contractors. It was not always the contractors' fault either! The first engineer of the London and Southampton Railway was Francis Giles, who had been so outspoken on the subject of Chat Moss during the Parliamentary battle over the Liverpool and Manchester Railway. It was not his first connection with the project of improved means of communication between London and Southampton. During the Napoleonic wars the hazards of navigation in the English Channel led to the idea of a ship canal between Portsmouth and London; it was duly investigated by John Rennie, and a survey was made by Giles. But in view of the sweeping statements and highly-coloured statistics contained in his evidence against the Liverpool and Manchester Railway it was perhaps no more than poetic justice that when he had the handling of a major project himself he proved quite unequal to the task. The contracts were let to numerous small men; several of them failed outright, while others were ill-chosen and intransigent. Before long the entire work was falling well behind schedule and bordering upon confusion. Giles was obliged to resign, and the directors thereupon took the prudent step of calling in Joseph Locke(18), and Locke in his turn called in Brassey.

The London and Southampton as finally constructed was a magnificent piece of railway, with an alignment that was ideal for sustained high-speed running, and with no very severe gradients. To maintain the even gradient some heavy earthworks were needed, in crossing the wild commons of north-west Surrey, and cutting through the Chobham Ridge; while in traversing the chalk downlands west of Basingstoke

18   Joseph Locke

*Both from photographs taken in
the last years of their lives*

19   Thomas Brassey

20   The stationary-engine house at Camden

21   Southern entrance to Watford Tunnel

22   Pumping machinery at Kilsby Tunnel
From drawings by J. C. Bourne, 1837

BUILDING THE LONDON AND BIRMINGHAM LINE

the rapid succession of cuttings, tunnels and great embankments as the train speeds downhill from Micheldever, through
Winchester to the estuary of the Itchen remains today one
of the most beautiful monuments to the engineering of
Locke, and the constructional work of Brassey. The London
terminus of the line was at first at Nine Elms about a mile
upstream from Vauxhall. In a contemporary account it is
picturesquely described as "a swampy district, occasionally
overflowed by the Thames. Its osier beds, pollards, wind-
mills and the river give it a Dutch aspect, but the ground is
fast becoming occupied with buildings, and losing its peculiar
character." At the southern end of the line there was no
direct way into Portsmouth; the nearest approach was at
first the branch from Eastleigh to Gosport. Here Brassey
ran into most unexpected trouble with the relatively short
tunnel near Fareham. Sir Frederick Smith, then Chief
Inspecting Officer of the Board of Trade described it thus:

These works pass through a soil which has baffled all calculations. In excavating, both in the cutting and tunnel, the workmen were obliged to blast a good proportion of the ground with
gunpowder, and yet, from exposure to wet, it has become almost
semi-fluid and in the cutting there is scarcely any slope at
which it would stand. At the north end of the tunnel the slopes
have, in consequence, lost all regularity of form and pour over
the retaining walls upon the rails.

In following the chequered pattern of railway development in Great Britain it is difficult to maintain a very strict
chronological order; and in pursuing the story of the great
association between Locke and Brassey, which developed
from their first meeting in constructional days on the Grand
Junction, the Southampton, which was not opened until
1840, has come in front of that most outstanding of early
English railways, the London and Birmingham. Actually
the Bill for this latter railway was passed in the same year as
that for the Grand Junction, namely 1833, and one year
ahead of the Southampton. But the Grand Junction, as its
name suggests, was so much linked up with the Liverpool
and Manchester from which it provided a connection to the
Black Country that it naturally comes first in this particular
account. In the general picture of railway development, as

6

it affected the industrial and commercial build-up of this country, the London and Birmingham is of vital importance as it was the first main line to enter the metropolis. In the north, lines had been authorised from Newcastle to Carlisle, in 1829, from Leeds to Selby in 1830; from Manchester to Sheffield in 1831; and there was a curious little railway from Bodmin to Wadebridge built expressly for the purpose of conveying sea-sand inland for manure. Also, in the same year that this first Cornish railway was authorised, in 1832, the Bill was passed for a narrow gauge line from the slate quarries of Festiniog to Portmadoc.

Despite the obvious success of the Liverpool and Manchester Railway, and the way that more and more projects were being laid before Parliament, the new mode of travel was still, in the "thirties" of last century looked upon generally as something to be confined to industrial districts, and not in any way to supersede the coach and the post-chaise. Whole sections of the Press were deadly antagonistic, and when London's first railway was opened, the local line to Greenwich in 1837, they fairly let themselves go. It is true that this line was in many ways regarded, and promoted as a stunt. Passenger traffic on the Liverpool and Manchester had been so unexpectedly great, and its fame so noised abroad that the London promoters felt that a good deal of business was to be had in the way of joy rides. Certainly the introduction of the train service was accompanied by a good deal of what we should now call "ballyhoo", and bands played the trains in and out of the terminal stations! Upon the opening of this first railway in London *John Bull* commented thus:

> Loss of life on that favourite toy from Liverpool to Manchester has always been terrific. Mr. Huskisson was the first martyr; and the last splendid exhibition took place on Thursday upon the new tomfoolery to Greenwich when "by some accident" one of the carriages in which a party of noodles ventured themselves was thrown off the rails, but though it ran a vast number of yards no serious accident occurred. How lucky! Nobody killed the first day!

But whatever ideas of stunts and joyriding may have been in the minds of the original promoters of the Greenwich line, no such fantasies could be tagged on to the London and Birmingham, which was authorised in the same year. Robert Stephenson was the engineer, though he did not secure the post without a good deal of preliminary competition. For one thing John Rennie the younger had some years earlier put forward a route of his own. Following his brief association with the Liverpool and Manchester Railway, and the encouragement and patronage he received from Viscount Lowther on the subject of railways generally, Rennie and his brother began to work out a comprehensive network of main lines connecting business centres in the country, and among these was a route from London through Birmingham to Liverpool. Rennie's route to Birmingham ran via Aylesbury, Bicester, Banbury, Kenilworth and Warwick, though it is hard to follow his argument that this line led through much less difficult country than that taken by Stephenson's line.

With the experience of locomotive working on the short, though steep gradients occurring in the middle section of the Liverpool and Manchester Railway, George Stephenson, his son, and Locke paid great attention to the art of securing an even gradient in the lines they built in the "thirties". On the London and Birmingham Robert Stephenson secured a maximum slope of 1 in 330 between Camden Town and the northern terminus, but this involved engineering works of unprecedented magnitude, cutting through the three ranges of hills that lay athwart the course (23). Tring cutting appears to have been no more than a great labour. By following the course of the Grand Junction Canal, and passing through the Chiltern Hills by the Tring gap, a good approach from the south was easily obtained. But on the north side the chalk escarpments which show up so finely when travelling southwards made an abrupt descent into the vale below, and to keep the gradient down to 1 in 330 an enormous cutting was made in the chalk, extending for nearly two miles north of Tring station. The next obstacle was the limestone ridge that runs north-eastwards from the Cotswolds, and which Stephenson attacked mid-way between Towcester and Northampton. Samuel Smiles describes Blisworth Cutting as one of the longest and deepest grooves ever cut in the

6*

23   Blisworth Cutting

solid earth. It is not quite so long as that at Tring, but far
deeper, and reaches a maximum depth of 65 ft. This very
depth brought unexpected difficulties; beneath the rock was
stiff clay, and beneath the clay a bed of loose shale so full of
water that for a time the works were completely flooded.
Even when the installation of large pumping engines had
countered the inward flow of water difficulty was experienced
in supporting the rock that had been exposed. The clay
tended to bulge out, and in the lower part of the cutting
massive retaining walls were built to keep the clay in place.
Deep though Blisworth Cutting originally was, the London
and North Western Railway deepened it still further on the
eastern side when the direct line to Northampton was built,
and two further running lines were added on a descending
gradient from Roade station.

By far the greatest and most troublesome work on the
London and Birmingham Railway, however, was the driving
of Kilsby Tunnel. The ridge here rose to some 160 ft. above
the proposed level of the railway and a tunnel $1\frac{1}{2}$ miles long
was needed. Trial borings were made to ascertain the nature

of the ground beneath the surface, and while these indicated shale and possible troubles with water they completely missed an extensive quicksand which existed beneath a bed of thick clay. It is interesting to speculate upon what tactics Robert Stephenson would have adopted if this extreme hazard had been known of earlier. As it was, the trial borings were enlarged to become working shafts, work was commenced in excavation and the quicksand was struck in the most dramatic and alarming manner. Without warning a deluge of water broke in, the works were flooded, and the men escaped only by swimming to the shaft. It was clear at once that water in such quantities could not be dealt with by any ordinary methods. Robert Stephenson sought his father's opinion, and while other engineers took the most pessimistic view and foretold complete abandonment George Stephenson was steadfastness itself, as in his own predicament at Chat Moss, and counselled the use of more, more and still more pumps until the inward flow of water was mastered by sheer force of machinery.

Robert Stephenson as the responsible engineer and with his eye, no doubt, on the ultimate cost, tried a short cut, rather against his father's advice. He suggested running a driftway inwards from the open hillside, to strike the quicksand and drain the water away in that manner. It was tried, and the danger point was approached; then the workmen were all withdrawn from the driftway. Before long a roar was heard as of distant thunder. It was hoped that the water had burst in, but to everyone's surprise very little water made its way to the open of the drift, and a cautious examination inside revealed that the water had certainly burst in, but in so doing had brought with it such a volume of sand that the whole driftway had been completely choked up! There was now nothing for it, but to pile on more and more pumps (22). During the next eight months the quantity of water removed averaged about 2,000 gallons per minute, and this was raised from a depth of 120 ft. Only by this colossal effort was it possible for the tunnel to be excavated, and eventually the overall cost came to more than £100 for every yard of railway through the tunnel. The prolongation of the work was viewed with dismay by the quiet hamlet of

24   Ventilating shafts, Kilsby Tunnel

Kilsby, and of the navvies Smiles says that here their pay-
nights were "a saturnalia of riot and disorder"! The local
clergyman did not take quite such a charitable view of them
as Mr. Dickson did, and tackled one ganger on the im-
propriety of Sunday work. Robert Stephenson in after years
used to enjoy relating the classic reply of the ganger, "Why
Soondays hain't cropt out here yet!"

Two very important lines in the Midlands next illustrate
the gradual development of railways in this country, the
Midland Counties Railway, of which Vignoles was the
engineer, and the North Midland, which was built by George
Stephenson. Neither involved any outstanding engineering
works, but in their situation and in the way they exemplified
the careers of the men who made them both have a deep
significance. The North Midland was one of the finest of all
George Stephenson's lines; to him it epitomised the industrial
development brought about by the coming of railways, and
he made his last home within sound of its trains. The town
of Derby was a natural junction point in the north-east
Midlands, and railways were being planned to enter it from

several directions; the main line to Yorkshire and North-Eastern England lay up the Derwent valley to Ambergate, and thence to Chesterfield, the Rother valley, Normanton and Leeds. It was a splendid route, laid out for fast running, and it tapped the chain of large collieries lying on the direct line. Sheffield lay in the higher and more difficult country to the west, and it was not so much by-passed as unnoticed as the line made its straight and level course north of Chesterfield. In later years the fact that Sheffield did lie off the most direct route was a godsend in operating the coal traffic, the bulk of which could be run clear of the city and its heavy passenger traffic. The principal line to the south now leaves the North Midland at Clay Cross and heads through the colliery districts of the Erewash valley. Now it is, in general, only the trains for the West of England that run the full length of the original North Midland line, and so traverse some of its most characteristic stretches.

Here Stephenson extended his activities, when sixty years of age, to that of colliery owner. In partnership with some of his Liverpool friends he took a lease of the Clay Cross estate, and pits were opened on a big scale. He also erected an enormous lime works at Ambergate, which, successful as it was, cut, however, a grievous scar into a delightful stretch of Derbyshire dale country. Tapton

25 On the North Midland Line
near Ambergate

26   Lime Works at Ambergate

House was included in the lease of one of the collieries.
It stood on a commanding height on the hill above Chesterfield, and there he made his home. It was very centrally
placed for all his later-life activities; the trains on the
North Midland line passed at the base of the hill, and the
eye ranging over the country could see the evidences of
industrial development springing up along the line of the
railway. Here indeed was the wealth of Britain being
realised, and here on a grand scale were steam locomotives
bringing forth that wealth on a trunk line of railway. George
Stephenson lived to see the North Midland amalgamated
with the Midland Counties and the Birmingham and Derby
to form the Midland Railway proper, and at that time it
still formed part of the main line from London to his native
Tyneside. Passengers travelling north from Euston saw some
glimpses of the Derbyshire dale country between the rock
cuttings and between the tunnels that came so frequently
along the southernmost part of the North Midland. They
would see also, and marvel at the scene if it was night, the
long range of Stephenson's lime kilns running abreast of the
line at Ambergate.

The connection from Derby to the South was made by the
Midland Counties Railway, running through Loughborough,

and Leicester, to join the London and Birmingham at Rugby.
Although this continued the line of communication between
London and the North-east, and was important as such, it
had, historically, a far greater significance from Vignoles's
advocacy of a new type of rail and foundation. Hitherto the
regular method had been to lay the rails upon stone blocks,
and the blocks themselves were laid by a very slow and
laborious process. The huge slabs, about 2 ft. square by
1 ft. thick, were laid diagonally to the line of railway, so that
the points of adjacent blocks practically touched. On the
Liverpool and Manchester Railway Stephenson had contrived to let the blocks set themselves and bed down by the
following procedure: a lever about 20 ft. long, mounted on a
portable stand, was used to lift the blocks. By means of a
chain device the block was lifted about 1 ft. from the ground
and then allowed to fall under its own weight. This was
repeated a number of times until the ground, by sheer
pummelling from the block, was made into a good seating.
How it was contrived to get all the blocks exactly level one
wonders indeed. There were no ties between the row of blocks
supporting one rail, and the row supporting the other.
Reliance was placed upon the bedding down of the blocks
themselves to maintain the correct gauge between the rails.

On clay soils, or embankments where the ground had not
fully consolidated, transverse sleepers of timber were used
in order to spread the load and increase the bearing surface.
But in the middle "thirties" these latter were regarded as
a makeshift, until the more solid foundation of a stone block
support could be installed. But that stone blocks left a good
deal to be desired is evident from the efforts of Vignoles and
others to get a better road. The riding was hard and uncomfortable, and the breakage of springs was frequent. On the
stone-block roads the rails were supported in the chairs
mounted on the top of the blocks. Vignoles endeavoured to
get better riding by supporting the rail throughout its length
on a longitudinal baulk of timber. With such a method of
mounting the existing type of rail was unsuitable, and he
designed a rail which, while having a running head similar
to that of existing rails, had also a broad base so as to rest
upon the longitudinal timber. Vignoles tried his level best

to get the directors of the Midland Counties to adopt this rail; but they were unwilling to depart from precedent and he was instructed to lay the track upon stone blocks. They were perhaps influenced by Joseph Locke's work on the Grand Junction where he had laid rails on a dumb-bell section, weighing no less than 62 lb. per yard, on the orthodox stone blocks. The aim was then rigidity, and Locke by use of his heavier rail section was doing in another way what Vignoles aimed at in his continuously supported flat-bottomed rail.

Mention of the stone blocks themselves maintaining the gauge, or width between the rails, leads on to the gauge itself. Stephenson's dictum was, make them all the same; the Stockton and Darlington, the Canterbury and Whitstable, and the Grand Junction might be a good way from each other, but he foretold the day when they would all be joined. And so a width of 4 ft. 8½ in. was used—this being the gauge of the Killingworth Colliery Railway. By a standing order in Parliament this gauge was at first made compulsory for all public lines of railway; but in 1836 this order, for some reason that is difficult to trace, was suspended, and the way was thus left clear for one of the most romantic, far-reaching and dramatic episodes in the history of British railways. Nicholas Wood writing two years after the suspension of the order says: "It is impossible to conceive the confusion, which may be the result of this departure, of the legislature from a standard width for all railways; especially if railway companies, and engineers, follow the dictates of their own opinion, without reference to the general convenience of the public." The result was some new railways in Scotland, built to a gauge of 5 ft. 6 in. and the outstanding example of the Great Western on which Isambard Brunel the younger used the exceptional gauge of 7 ft.

It was inevitable that, sooner or later, "Mr. Brunel, Junr." as he was generally referred to in those days (1), would enter the field of railway construction; though one would imagine that few, even among those who knew his original turn of mind and vivid personality, could have foreseen the positive upheaval he caused in the chain of railway development in this country. The Great Western Railway was born in Bristol, and it was by a curious chain of circumstances that

Brunel happened to be there at the critical time, and was already well known in the city. Some years earlier his father had been very deeply involved with his task of building the tunnel under the River Thames. Young Isambard had been his assistant, and when the second great irruption of water took place in January 1828, he was so seriously injured as to need constant medical attention for several months. Work on the Thames Tunnel was at a complete standstill, and after recuperating young Brunel was at something of a loose end for some time. He paid a visit to the West of England, and while there heard of the proposal to build a bridge over the Avon at Bristol. How Brunel's design came to be accepted, in preference to one submitted by Telford of all engineers, is another story; but as a result Brunel was already well-known in Bristol when the time came for the railway project to be launched, and there is no doubt that the prominent business men of the city numbered among the promoters were deeply impressed by his enthusiasm and his straightforward advocacy. There was no bluff in the make-up of Isambard Kingdom Brunel. At one stage of the preliminary negotiations he learnt that it was the intention of the Bristol committee to appoint as engineer the man who would give the lowest estimate for the building of the line. He was then no more than twenty-six years of age, and yet with courage and professional acumen far beyond his years he withdrew his application for the post, saying that, "such a criterion merely put a premium on flattering promises and would appeal most to the man who had little reputation to lose and cared least about losing what he already had." He secured the appointment, as from March 1833.

In his outlook he differed profoundly in many important respects from the engineers of the Stephenson school. Brought up in the very hard conditions of pioneer days George Stephenson and his pupils were thrifty and hard-headed, suiting their practice to the depth of the purse available. Joseph Locke in particular had a perfect genius for economy in laying out a route. Brunel, on the other hand, was an idealist. Nothing was good enough for him except the very best, and his vision of railway speed in the future made necessary, in his eyes, something on a grander scale by far than the lines already open, or projected(14). The carriages must be wider, so as to convey more passengers; the wagons must be larger to take bigger loads of merchandise(28), and a wider gauge of rails would not only permit of this, but more important of all would allow of a much more convenient arrangement of the engine machinery. How right he was! What benefits a 7-ft. gauge would have conferred upon us when locomotives had grown to their present size!(36). He carried the Great Western board with him, and the line was built to the 7-ft. gauge, but from that very first decision difficulties began. Brunel realised that sooner or later there would be difficulties at points where traffic was interchanged with other lines; but he also hoped for a complete 7-ft. gauge monopoly in the south and west of England. I think, too, that there was no doubt in his mind that once the "broad gauge" was in operation on the Great Western, its advantages would be so apparent that all future main lines would be built up to his standard.

It is, however, unfortunately much easier to standardise at the level of the lowest rather than of the highest. This took place over many items of railway equipment at the time of the grouping in 1923, and it has taken place since nationalisation on a larger scale. Those maintaining the highest standards are usually in a minority and relaxations can be more expediently imposed; to bring the majority up to the standards of the few would be a colossal task. Brunel has been accused of a serious lack of judgment—even of profligate waste of the Company's resources. His misjudgment, if one can call it such, was one of human nature and timing rather than of engineering. Had it been introduced three or four years earlier the broad gauge might have won the day. Its actual introduction on the Great Western, and its extension into South Wales, Devon and Cornwall ushered in a period of spaciousness and romance in railway travel; but inevitably it put the Great Western into a position of isolation so far as the other railways of the country were concerned. And although the broad gauge finally disappeared more than sixty years ago that atmosphere of isolation has never quite disappeared. Even in recent times at inter-railway gatherings one has heard the

27   Crewe Station, L. & N.W.R.
From a lithograph by F. Tait

28   Bath Station, G.W.R.
From a drawing by J. C. Bourne, 1846

29, 30   Two contemporary photographs of the Bridge during construction

Designed by I. K. Brunel, 1859

ROYAL ALBERT BRIDGE, SALTASH

Great Western representatives addressed colloquially as "you broad-gauge blokes!"

The complications arising as a result of the broad gauge belong to a considerably later date than that with which we are now concerned; but at the time of construction of the Great Western Railway Brunel made another innovation in his method of laying the permanent way. All engineers of that period sought rigidity for the track. The stone blocks of the earliest line were made progressively larger and heavier on subsequent railways, and I have told earlier how Vignoles proposed laying his flat-bottomed rail on continuous baulks of timber. But while Vignoles failed to carry his directors with him on the Midland Counties Railway, Brunel received authority for a very similar method of construction on the Great Western. His "bridge" rail was, in effect, the same as Vignoles design, and he adopted the longitudinal timbers; but Brunel's special contribution lay in his method of obtaining extra rigidity. To counteract any possible effects of subsidence on embankments and stretches of soft ground, massive piles were driven down to reach the firm virgin ground below any formation that had been built up to maintain the gradient of the railway. The sleepers, while packed round with the ballast, rested on the piles, and very great care was taken to make the top absolutely level. The piles were driven to the exact depth required; no portion was allowed to be cut off, and if any one did not drive to the depth required it had to be drawn out and driven in again. The cross timbers were bolted to the piles, and the longitudinals laid on the top.

When the bolting up was complete and the top surface as level as could be contrived, an extraordinary process was followed in order to secure the utmost rigidity. Sand, or fine gravel was then packed or beaten in below the longitudinals and the cross timbers; it was packed to such an extent that the longitudinals were forced up between the point of attachment to the cross timbers, sometimes to the extent of three-quarters of an inch. When the timbers had all been thoroughly packed up, and rammed and strained to the utmost the upper surface of the longitudinals was planed down to one uniform level, and then after the rails had been

7

fixed into position a heavy roller, weighing about ten tons was passed over each length two or three times, and all fastenings tightened up where ever possible. The result was a very fine, very rigid track. And at this stage, at about the turn of the year 1838, we can conveniently leave constructional matters for a time in order to look, in a little more detail, at the developments of the steam locomotive.

Before doing so, however, there is a good story of Brunel to be told. During constructional days on the Great Western intense opposition to the railway was shown by all those interested in coaching on the Bath Road. In the ordinary way Brunel took not the slightest notice of all this, but on one occasion he was very nearly tempted into making an amusing reprisal. The story goes that he and some of his assistants were staying at one of the inns at Calne, under the western escarpments of the Marlborough Downs; and things got to the pitch that one of his assistants was goaded into suggesting: "It would serve them right if we changed the White Horse into a locomotive!" The White Horse of Cherhill is a prominent landmark on the downs above Calne, and can actually be glimpsed from the train near Chippenham. Anyhow Brunel was highly amused at the idea; more than that, he began at once to scheme out how it could be done in a single night—how many men would be needed to make the alterations to the pattern cut in the short turf, how the gangs would be organised, and so on. He even went to the extent of discussing how smoke could be made to issue from the chimney! One can imagine how his tremendous sense of fun delighted in the prospect of the sensation that would be caused. It was no mere whim of a single night; the operation was planned in complete detail, but it was never carried out. How this glorious "leg-pull" lapsed is not related. At that time the Office of Works had not yet begun the preservation of ancient monuments, and there were no Town and Country Planning restrictions hanging over an exuberant band like the Sword of Damocles. In all probability the explanation was simple enough: more urgent business supervened.

CHAPTER III

Locomotives and Locomotive Men

T HE building of the *Rocket* and its successful running in the Rainhill trials may well be considered as the great turning point in early locomotive history. Until then the old "puffers" had trundled along at low speeds over short distances. Even the 20-mile main line of the Stockton and Darlington had extended them to their limit, and for a time the resolute optimism of George Stephenson was hardly supported by the day-to-day work of his engines in the hauling of the coal trains. His vision of a railway network covering the whole country needed some solid backing in greater and more sustained steaming capacity, and greater freedom of running. It is, of course, easy to lay down such desiderata when casting the mind back, in retrospect, over 125 years of continuous development; but the Stephensons, father and son, while sufficiently aware of the operating difficulties on the Stockton and Darlington chose to take a broader view. While Timothy Hackworth struggled to keep things going on the line with the limited equipment available in the repair sheds at Shildon, George Stephenson had more particularly in mind the future motive power requirements of the Liverpool and Manchester. It was perhaps inevitable that in after years Hackworth felt that he had received the "rough end of the stick": that he pulled the Stephenson chestnuts out of the fire only to receive a very public rebuff at Rainhill. Although one would not go so far as to say that a feud developed between the two families, the Hackworths and Stephensons were henceforth keen rivals instead of allies.

In the previous chapter I referred to the *Royal George*, built by Timothy Hackworth at Shildon in 1827. This was the largest and heaviest engine to be constructed at that time; it provided the power needed for working the coal

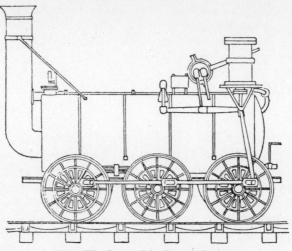

31   Hackworth's *Royal George*

trains by use of a much larger boiler than any Stephenson
himself had so far built, and by having six wheels coupled.
But the large boiler in itself did not provide the entire answer.
Hackworth increased the steaming capacity by arranging the
flue from the fire-box to the chimney in the form of a U,
instead of a single large pipe, and so presented an increased
area of flue tube in contact with the water. It is also generally
agreed nowadays that Hackworth was the inventor of the
blast pipe as we know it today—a narrowing cone, through
the nozzle of which the exhaust steam passes at high velocity
and creates an intense draught on the fire. Stephenson had
previously used what he called "an exarsting pipe", extending nearly to the top of the chimney, and at a much earlier
date Richard Trevithick got very close to the same arrangement. In the nineteenth century intense controversy raged
upon who had the strongest claim to be called the inventor.
Samuel Smiles was the self-appointed champion of George
Stephenson; Francis Trevithick argued his father's claim,
while John Wesley Hackworth stoutly defended the achievement of his father. In any case the use of the blast pipe on
the *Royal George* made that engine very free steaming, while
the six-coupled wheels eliminated the old trouble of slipping
on wet rails, or on a gradient.

Outwardly the wheels were perhaps the most distinctive feature of the *Royal George*, and although the design was nothing more than an ingenious make-shift to suit the manufacturing facilities at his disposal Hackworth's design remained standard on the Stockton and Darlington freight engines for the ensuing twenty years. In the *Royal George* the wheels were 4 ft. in diameter. There were no lathes in the Shildon shops large enough to turn up the rims when the wheels were fixed on the axles, and so Hackworth made the wheels in two parts. The inner portion including the boss was made in cast-iron, and as large as the lathe would take; this "centre" was trued up, and then the outer section was fitted, and trued to the inner portion, the two sections being held together by a series of wooden keys. A beautiful example of Stockton and Darlington six-coupled goods engines having the Hackworth type of plug-wheel has been preserved, and now stands on a pedestal in Darlington station. This is the *Derwent*, which was built by Alfred Kitching in 1839.

Another unusual feature, common to the *Royal George* and to later Stockton and Darlington coal engines was that the fire-door was at the chimney end of the boiler. This was made necessary on the *Royal George* by the U-shaped flue, which started from the fire-box, ran the length of the boiler, and returned again to the chimney. As a result these Hackworth engines had to be provided with two tenders; one, on which the fireman rode, was propelled ahead of the engine, while the second, with the driver, was in the conventional position between the engine and the train. It is extraordinary to realise that locomotives of this type were built down to the year 1846, and that some were still in regular service on the Stockton and Darlington Railway at the time of the Jubilee celebrations of 1875.

The success of the *Royal George* emboldened Hackworth to enter the competition staged by the directors of the Liverpool and Manchester Railway in opposition to his friends and associates the Stephensons. The circumstances were enough to daunt the boldest and most determined of pioneers. As engineer and manager of the Stockton and Darlington Railway he was not a free agent. The designing of the engine for the competition had to be done in his spare time, and although the Company allowed him to erect the engine in the Shildon shops it had to be done at his own expense. The boiler was made at Bedlington Ironworks, the cylinders were cast at Stephenson's works. Some of his suppliers were late with their deliveries, and the erection of the engine was done hurriedly in order to reach Rainhill in time for the trials. Before the actual competition there was little opportunity for any thorough testing, and a few midnight runs on the level stretch of the line near Aycliffe were all that was possible in the time. As a courageous piece of pioneer locomotive construction Hackworth's *Sans Pareil* can have few equals. But before coming to the special features of this brave little engine some reference is needed to the test conditions imposed by the Liverpool and Manchester Railway.

The conditions were stated in a circular issued from the Railway Office, Liverpool, on April 25th, 1829. They included a number of general provisions, such as safety valves, springs, and so on, plus the important one that the engine must "effectually consume its own smoke". The maximum weight of the engine only, with a full complement of water in the boiler, was not to exceed 6 tons, though a lighter engine was preferred. If the engine exceeded 4½ tons in weight it was to be carried on six wheels. The working steam pressure in the boiler was not to exceed 50 lb. per sq. in., and in such conditions certain train loads were specified for a speed of 10 m.p.h. according to the weight of the engine itself: a 6-ton engine was required to haul 20 tons; a 5-ton engine, 15 tons, and so on.

32   Hackworth's *Sans Pareil*

Lastly the price was not to exceed £550. The engines entered for the competition were to be delivered at the Liverpool end of the railway not later than October 1st, 1829. As the time approached three eminent engineers of the day, Rastrick, John Kennedy of Manchester, and Nicholas Wood were appointed judges, and of these Wood(3) has handed down to posterity very complete details of the trials in his classic work, *A Practical Treatise on Railroads*.

The running ground chosen was a stretch of level track on the Manchester side of Rainhill bridge. The test length was $1\frac{3}{4}$ miles long, but this included one-eighth of a mile at each end for starting and stopping. The central portion of $1\frac{1}{2}$ miles was to be covered at full speed. To similate service conditions as far as possible each competitor was required to make ten return trips over the course in rapid succession. Thus a total of 30 miles would be covered at full speed, and this was approximately equal to a run from Liverpool to Manchester. After the test was completed more fuel and water was to be taken on, and ten more return trips made. There were no facilities for turning, and so half the runs over the measured $1\frac{1}{2}$ miles were made with the competing engines propelling their trains. As it turned out this had some effect upon the running speeds recorded. Samuel Smiles published a drawing by an imaginative artist of the day, which shows three locomotives racing on parallel tracks. Actually, as Nicholas Wood writes: "it was determined, to avoid confusion, that each engine should be tried separately, and on different days". There was excitement enough as it was, without the extra stimulus of a direct race!

Four steam locomotives were entered for the prize, and one horse machine. In addition to the *Rocket* and the *Sans Pareil*, there was the unconventional *Novelty*, entered by the Swedish inventor, Ericsson, in conjunction with John Braithwaite. In this enterprise they were joined by Charles Vignoles, who gave them considerable financial assistance. The *Novelty* had a vertical boiler and the necessary draught for rapid steam raising was provided for by a set of mechanically worked bellows. There was only one cylinder, fixed almost vertically above the rear pair of wheels. The fourth locomotive, the *Perseverance* built by Mr. Burstall was quite

33   The *Novelty*

outclassed, and took little or no part in the competition. Robert Stephenson, his father, and Locke regarded the *Novelty* as their most serious rival, and Vignoles in his eyewitness account of the trials records that: "the machinery was of much more finished workmanship than Stephenson's engine, and when it was brought to view burnished with copper and dark blue paint, it evoked universal admiration". The *Novelty* was certainly the popular favourite. The local newspapers eulogised it as "exhibiting by its beauty and compactness the very *beau-ideal* of a locomotive"; and when on a preliminary run without any load it swept past the Rainhill grandstand at 23 m.p.h. it became more than ever the favourite. But Locke and George Stephenson looked on critically, and when on the return trip the bellows failed and the *Novelty* came to stand in mid-course George Stephenson turned to Locke and said, "Eh mon, we needn't fear yon thing, it's got no goots!"

The *Rocket* was an exceedingly simple and straightforward engine. Unlike the earlier Stephenson machines and Hackworth's *Sans Pareil*, it had but a single pair of driving wheels, with a pair of carrying wheels underneath the driver's footplate. The really novel feature was the boiler. To promote rapid evaporation by increasing the hot surfaces in contact with the water the flue from the fire-box to the chimney was split up, so that the hot gases of combustion instead of passing through one large pipe passed through a nest of much smaller ones. Nicholas Wood's drawing shows twenty-five flue tubes. This arrangement, adopted at the suggestion of Henry Booth, gave Robert Stephenson some anxious moments in the constructional stages. The difficulty lay in fitting the tubes, which were of copper, to the boiler ends without leakage occurring. Whether or not the *Rocket* as tested at Rainhill, had the new type of blast-pipe is difficult to decide. In his book *Timothy Hackworth and the Locomotive* Robert Young says definitely not. But the fact remains that the *Rocket* steamed very freely, though apparently its outward appearance was not to the liking of the spectators—however smartly turned out it was, in yellow and black with white chimney. The *Sans Pareil* turned the scale at $4\frac{3}{4}$ tons, and should, by the rules of the contest, have been carried on six wheels. The *Rocket* weighed $4\frac{1}{4}$ tons and the *Novelty* 3 tons 1 cwt.

The opening day of the test may be described in the words of Vignoles:

First day, October 6th, 1829 (Tuesday)

Place: Manchester side of the Skewbridge at Rainhill, on the level of one and three quarter miles, on which each competing engine was to make ten double journeys, or thirty-five miles in all, rather more than the distance between the two towns. Vast numbers of people were present. The "Rocket" first to try: it drew 12 tons 9 cwt. at exact rate of ten miles four chains per hour; without load it ran eighteen miles per hour. Its velocity was very unequal, and it did not at first thoroughly consume its own smoke.

For precise details of the actual performances we may turn to Nicholas Wood's account. The running was timed to the last second, and the logs of the two experiments, representing the journey from Liverpool to Manchester and back, include notes of the instant at which water was taken, the engine

34　The *Rocket*

was oiled, the pistons greased, and so on. The *Rocket* performed with complete reliability, and her two trips gave the following results for the 30 miles covered at full speed: first, experiment, average speed 13·4 m.p.h.; second experiment 14·2 m.p.h. On examining the details of individual runs it was found that the 1½-mile stretches in the eastbound direction were invariably done faster than the corresponding westbound runs. The carriages were being propelled in the westbound direction and it would certainly seem that the resistance to motion was greater in this method of working. Nicholas Wood felt that too much notice should not be taken of the performance when propelling, as no train would ordinarily be worked in this way. He accordingly took the average of all the eastbound runs made by the *Rocket*, and these gave a speed of 15 m.p.h. But in any case the requirements of the "ordeal", as it was called, had been fulfilled, without making any allowance for the abnormality of propelling, and it remained to be seen how the other competitors would fare.

Next came the *Sans Pareil*. It was duly weighed before starting on any run, but when found to scale 4 tons 15½ cwt. it was at once realised that one stipulated condition had not been complied with—namely that if a competing engine weighed more than 4½ tons it should be carried on six wheels. On consideration the judges determined to put the engine through its trials, and if its performance was satisfactory some recommendation might be made regarding its claim for the prize. The *Sans Pareil* started well, and at first her speeds averaged much the same as those of the *Rocket* with the same variation between eastbound and westbound running. But then Nicholas Wood writes: "In traversing the eighth trip to the west, the pump that supplies the boiler with water got wrong, which, checking the supply, the water in the boiler got below the top of the tube, and melted the leaden plug, inserted for the purpose of preventing accidents in such a case and put an end to the experiment." And of the *Sans Pareil* Wood says no more. Robert Young in his book *Timothy Hackworth and the Locomotive* naturally builds up the strongest possible case for the engine, though some of the data he quotes is at variance with the data published by

Wood. He states, for example, that the *Sans Pareil* hauled a load of 25 tons; actually the load was 19 tons 2 cwt. inclusive of the weight of the engine itself. The load given to the engine was in exact proportion to the engine weight, as it had been with the *Rocket*.

From Nicholas Wood's account it seems clear that it was the failure of the feed pump that finished the *Sans Pareil*; but Young says that one of the cylinders burst. Some difficulty had evidently been experienced with the casting of these cylinders at Stephenson's works, and six were made before two perfect ones were obtained. The defect lay in the casting of the internal port-way which ran the length of the cylinder. During casting the sand core had shifted, with the result that at this particular point the cylinder wall instead of being $\frac{7}{8}$ in. thick was only $\frac{1}{16}$ in. Young then records: "The consequence was that the engine had no sooner commenced working than the cylinder burst, when the race had to be run with one perfect cylinder only, whilst the fracture of the other opened at every stroke a direct communication between the boiler and the chimney." It is strange that Wood does not even mention this mishap, while Vignoles—a very shrewd observer—does not mention the *Sans Pareil* at all in his account of the trials.

From the recorded timings of Nicholas Wood it does not seem as if there was any steady deterioration of performance, as one might expect from a failure such as that described by Young, and her eighth and last run in the eastbound direction in 5 min. 31 sec. was the second fastest in the series. There had been a stop at the end of the sixth eastbound run to repair "the forcing pump", according to Wood's log, but the lead plug was not melted until the eighth westbound trip. Samuel Smiles relates that Hackworth pleaded with the judges for a further trial, presumably after a new cylinder had been fitted; but his request was declined on the dual grounds that the engine was over the stipulated weight, and that the sharp blast blew a large amount of burning coke into the air. Certainly consumption of fuel was very high—692 lb. per hour, against 217 lb. with the *Rocket*. From Young's account it might seem that part of this profligate waste was due to the defect in the cylinder; but if this was so it is

surprising that so precise and fair an observer as Wood took
no account of it in presenting his figures.

In the meantime the *Novelty* had been putting up some
spectacular, if erratic performances. She was dogged by
numerous small failures, and never completed a single series
of trials. Vignoles writes of October 10th.

> It was three o'clock when the "Novelty" was again fit to
> run, and her performance also was not deemed competitive.
> She drew a total weight of 10 tons 6 cwt. and one quarter,
> inclusive of her own weight. I rode on the engine and carefully
> timed her performance. She went her first distance at seventeen
> and a half miles per hour, and then discarded the load for a
> wagon full of forty-five passengers, which she whirled along at
> upwards of thirty miles an hour.

Charles Fox, who afterwards built the Crystal Palace, was
a spectator, and used to say he could never forget the look
on Robert Stephenson's face as the *Novelty* shot by the
Rocket. Really, however, Stephenson had nothing to fear,
and on his second series of runs, while maintaining a comfortable margin in hand over the stipulated speed it is evident
that the *Rocket* was far from being pressed to its utmost. On
the eastbound runs, over the measured 1½ miles, he had
averaged 14·4, 15·1, 17·0, 12·7, 14·8, 15·4, 14·6, 16·7, and
16·6 m.p.h. on nine successive runs; but on the last he
opened out, and with the full test load he put up an average
speed of 24·1 m.p.h.

From one cause or another neither the *Sans Pareil* nor the
Novelty completed a single set of trials, and the judges
naturally awarded the prize to the Stephensons and Henry
Booth. This outcome left Ericsson and Hackworth very
disappointed men. Ericsson was annoyed that mechanical
failures of a really minor kind had prevented his engine
from staying the course, when it was so obvious that it
could have fulfilled the conditions. Right up to the end the
Novelty remained the popular favourite, and further trials
were continued on the Liverpool and Manchester line. On
December 17th, 1829, Ericsson wrote to Braithwaite:

> We have been at work steadily the whole day, and everything
> has gone extremely well. . . . We went at various speeds during

the day, sometimes with and sometimes without passengers, and the steam was kept up in wonderful style.

The engine did not exceed two hundred and sixty strokes per minute, not quite forty miles an hour; and I am confident that if I dare trust the *force pump* at such a rate I could have done *one mile in one minute!*

As the engine passed on in its velocity the spectators cheered in a glorious manner. I will send the particulars of more experiments tomorrow.

Forty miles per hour in 1829: railway travel was certainly progressing!

While Ericsson and Braithwaite persevered with the *Novelty* over the very scene of their discomfiture earlier in the year, Timothy Hackworth had reason to feel very sore over the Rainhill trials. A faulty feed pump could have been made to work in time to complete the series of runs, but a fractured cylinder was another matter. And the fact that the cylinder came from Stephenson's works did not soften Hackworth's feelings towards the winners of the prize. On his behalf it is claimed that the failure was no fault of the design; in these days, however, a design of any kind that gave inordinate trouble in manufacture would not be considered a good one, and it does seem that the cylinders of the *Sans Pareil* come in this category. One can, I think, dismiss the contemporary insinuations from some quarters that the result of the Rainhill trials was a foregone conclusion, and that the *Sans Pareil* was sabotaged. In an event that created such enormous public interest it was inevitable that feelings should run high at times, and the feeling of injustice nursed for many years afterwards by Timothy Hackworth, had a strange parallel in 1925 when engine trials took place between the Great Western and the London and North Eastern Railways.

The success of the *Rocket* not only ensured the position of the locomotive on railways generally, but it also established the basic design that exists to this day. Critics of steam traction are apt to deride the old-fashioned "Puffing Billies", on which, so they say, little advance in technique has been made since Stephenson's time. But while it certainly is the simplest form of steam locomotive, basically no different from the *Rocket*, that has stood the test of time, the improvements made in the intervening years are far more than those of mere size. Not only has the haulage capacity increased enormously in relation to the weight of the engine, but the economy has improved. This latter is best represented by the coal burnt per hour for every horse-power exerted in hauling the train, and the figures relating to certain outstanding trials are given below to indicate something of the development that has followed the successful working of the *Rocket*.

LOCOMOTIVE PERFORMANCE DEVELOPMENT

Year	Railway	Engine	Weight of engine only tons	Load inc. tender tons	Train weight to engine weight	Length of test miles	Av. speed m.p.h.	Coal burnt per draw-bar horse-power hr./lb.
1829	Liverpool and Manchester	*Rocket*	4½	12¾	3	30	15	—
1906	North Eastern	*Smith's Compound Atlantic*	73½	517	7	80	53½	4½
1953	B.R. Western Region	*King Edward VII*	89	845	9½	73½	56¾	3

The tests of 1906 and 1953 were made with exceptional loads, but they are represented to show what locomotives of the highest quality can do, when required. Whereas the *Rocket* took three times its own weight, averaged 15 m.p.h., and could spurt to 24 m.p.h. for a short distance, the "King" class engine of the Great Western Railway, on one of the most severe tests ever set to a British locomotive, hauled nine and a half times its own weight, and ran at speeds of 70 m.p.h. and over, on level stretches of the line. Moreover the basic fuel consumption shows a considerable reduction over that of the North Eastern engine of 1906. Yet while *King Edward VII* incorporates very many refinements of design, of materials, and of manufacturing technique, the principle on which it operates is nothing more nor less than that of the *Rocket*.

The outcome of the Rainhill trials gave a tremendous fillip to railways, and from that time onwards it can be said that a new race of men was born—locomotive men. Robert Stephenson himself was by that time well experienced in the craft, but while he continued to guide the fortunes of the great firm that bore his name his interests spread so widely, and his services as a civil engineer became ultimately in such demand that his active participation gradually lessened. With Joseph Locke it was much the same, though in his case the post of engineer-in-chief to the Grand Junction Railway included responsibility for the locomotive department, with results to be described later. But whatever responsibilities he may have held in this direction Locke, no more that Vignoles, Braithwaite, or even George Stephenson himself, could never be regarded as an out-and-out locomotive man. The distinguished "father" of the breed was unquestionably Timothy Hackworth, who despite his great disappointment at Rainhill remained faithful to locomotives all his life; and he certainly lived to build some very fine ones. From 1830 onwards, however, so many engine building firms sprang into existence, and so many engines of all shapes and sizes were produced, that even today, viewing this phenomenon at a distance of more than a hundred years it is difficult to pick out the essential milestones in the development without getting bogged-down in a welter of detail. In any case I am concerned more with engineers than with engines. So, rather than trace the progress of the locomotive itself we turn to the young men of the day who were to make their mark in later years.

When writing of the Canterbury and Whitstable Railway I have already mentioned Edward Fletcher. At the time the Liverpool and Manchester was opened, in 1830, he was a young man of twenty-three, and already engaged up to the hilt in locomotive engineering. Then there was Alexander Allan, two years his junior, who joined the Stephenson's at Forth Street works, Newcastle, in 1832. One can well imagine how the new form of travel appealed to the younger generation of the day, though the attitude of many parents was indifferent, if nothing else. In her girlhood my mother knew an old lady who recalled vividly the opening of the

Grand Junction Railway. The quiet Cheshire country-side where she lived was agog with excitement as the day approached, so much so that her father deemed it wise for his family not to attend. The younger generation protested, but Papa was not to be moved; threats of disobedience were followed by counter-threats, and when the day dawned she and her two brothers were locked severally in upper rooms in that big country house. How she escaped, and had a splendid view of the opening of the railway is a longer story than can be told here! Some years later the man she married, a draughtsman in Crewe works, was associated with the great invention of water troughs. Those were the days of John Ramsbottom, one of the greatest locomotive engineers of the mid-Victorian period, and one revels in the story of him as a lad of sixteen journeying from Todmorden into Manchester to see the opening of the Liverpool and Manchester Railway. While Alexander Allan went to Stephenson's, Ramsbottom joined the new firm of Sharp, Roberts and Co. in Manchester and was there when competition was keen for orders and the whole industry was new and thrusting.

It was certainly a coincidence that four others, all men who came to play an important part in the development of the locomotive were born in the same year, 1816: Thomas Crampton, Daniel Gooch, Robert Sinclair and Archibald Sturrock. Their careers eventually became as diverse as could be imagined. Gooch was born at Bedlington, in the very shadow of the ironworks that rolled the wrought-iron rails for the Stockton and Darlington, and built some of the early locomotive boilers; Sturrock was a native of Forfarshire, who began work as an apprentice at the East Foundry in Dundee, in 1832. Crampton, on the other hand, was born in much more exalted circumstances, at Broadstairs; he was educated at one of those private schools of the day that catered for the sons of gentlemen, and while Gooch and Sturrock were in the thick of it by the year 1832, Crampton's early career was more leisured and it was not until 1839 that he took a post under Sir Marc Brunel. Then, whereas Crampton became closely associated with both Sturrock and Gooch, Robert Sinclair's early training led him in due course into the opposite camp. As a public schoolboy, at Charterhouse, he was a contemporary of John Leech and W. M. Thackeray; but on leaving school he at once took up an engineering training, and afterwards he took a job on the Grand Junction Railway, in the old Edge Hill works, just outside Liverpool, where of course he came under the powerful influence of Joseph Locke, and of Alexander Allan. From this "school" came the "Old Crewe" tradition, which was to extend from the London and North Western to the Caledonian, the Highland and to East Anglia.

In the North Eastern counties of England Timothy Hackworth continued his own development on the Stockton and Darlington. In Newcastle the sons of Robert Hawthorn, Stephenson's "great enemy" in the West Moor days, set up a manufactory of their own, and in due course produced some fine engines; while within hailing distance of the Liverpool and Manchester Railway there began Fairbairn's, Tayleur and Co., and Beyer, Peacock and Co. Of course the oldest firm of them all, Robert Stephenson and Co., had a good start over their competitors, and at one time they were supplying locomotives to almost every railway in the country. By the middle thirties, however, the centre of interest moved from the north to the Great Western, as engineers awaited the outcome of Brunel's successful advocacy of a much wider gauge. In June 1836 he wrote to certain builders of locomotives inviting tenders for two engines, but apart from specifying that they should be at least equal to the best then running on the Liverpool and Manchester Railway he seems to have left all the features of detail design to the builders. In due course orders for twenty locomotives were placed with various firms, with the result that the G.W.R. started with a highly assorted lot. Some were undeniably freaks, and since drawings had been submitted before each order one comes to the conclusion that the appraisal of locomotive design was not one of Brunel's strongest points.

It was at about this time that Daniel Gooch wrote his famous letter to Brunel. It is worth quoting in full:

Manchester and Leeds Railway Office
Rochdale. July 18th./37

I. K. Brunel Esq.,
    Dear Sir,
        I have just been informed it is your intention to erect an Engine Manufactory at or near Bristol and that you wish to engage a person as Manager. I take the earliest opportunity of offering my services for the situation.

I have until the last two months been constantly engaged in engine building and have worked at each branch of the business but principally at Locomotive Engine Work. The first three years of my time I was with Mr. Homphry at the Tredegar Iron Works, Monmouthshire. I left him to go to Mr. R. Stephenson and was at the Vulcan Foundry 12 months when I obtained leave from Mr. Stephenson to go down to Mr. Stirling of the Dundee Foundry Co. Dundee to get a knowledge of steamboat work. I remained with him 12 months and returned to Mr. Stephenson's works at Newcastle where I remained until last October when I left, having had an offer from a party in Newcastle to take the Management of a locomotive Manufactory which they intended erecting but which owing to some unavoidable circumstances they have now given up the idea of proceeding with and we have countermanded the order for machinery. This left me without a situation and I am anxious to engage myself to some Company where I will have the management of the building of engines. At present I am with my brother on the Manchester and Leeds Line, where I have employment until I meet with something more suitable.

I will be glad to refer you to any of the forementioned places for testimonials.

Should you approve of my application I shall be glad to hear from you stating the salary and any other information you may think necessary.
                    I am, Sir,
                        Yours Obly.
                        DANL. GOOCH.

He was appointed locomotive assistant to Brunel, and exactly one month after the date of his application he took up his duties on the Great Western Railway. He was not yet twenty-one years of age, while Brunel himself was then only thirty-two!

In the short time he had been at the Dundee Foundry

Gooch had met Archibald Sturrock, who was serving his
apprenticeship there as a mechanic. But the short period of
their first acquaintance was not too short to blossom into a
strong friendship, and Gooch found time to teach Sturrock
the art of mechanical drawing. The sequel to this was that
in 1841 the young Scots mechanic joined the Great Western
as principal assistant to Gooch. Sturrock was a "go-getter"
of no mean ability: just the man to back up such a pair as
Brunel and Gooch. They needed all the assistance they
could get, with the eyes of the engineering world upon the
broad gauge. The opening of the line was very nearly
disastrous. Many years later Gooch wrote of his appointment:

> None of the engines had then been delivered, although
> several were ordered. My first work was to prepare plans for
> the engine-houses at Paddington and Maidenhead, and then
> I went to inspect the engines then building. I was not much
> pleased with the design of the engines ordered. They had very
> small boilers and cylinders, and very large wheels. . . .

Brunel was a great personal friend of Robert Stephenson's;
but presumably due to pressure of orders from other railways
the Forth Street works did not build any engines specially
for the Great Western. Six came from Mather, Dixon and
Co. of Liverpool; six from Tayleurs; two from Hawthorn's;
three from Sharp Roberts; and two from the Haigh Foundry,
Wigan. Then by a lucky chance Stephenson's had on their
hands two engines constructed to the order of the New
Orleans Railway, and Brunel snapped them up, writing to
Robert Stephenson: "I look forward to having such an engine
as never before." The first of these two, the *North Star*,
was shipped from the Tyne to London, and conveyed thence
up the Thames by barge to Maidenhead. Brunel, with
characteristic enthusiasm wrote to a friend: "We have a
splendid engine of Stephenson's; it would have been a
beautiful ornament in the most elegant drawing-room."
Gooch was more guarded in his comments:

> On 31st. May 1838, [he wrote concerning the line to Maiden-
> head], the directors made their first trip over the whole length
> of this portion, and it was opened to the public on the 4th June,

and then my difficulties with the engines began. The "North Star" and the six from the Vulcan Foundry Company were the only ones I could depend upon. For many weeks my nights were spent in a carriage in the engine-house at Paddington, as repairs had to be done to the engines at night to get them to do their work next day. The "North Star" being the most powerful one and in other respects the best, was my chief reliance, but she was often getting into trouble from other causes.

Young Gooch must have had a hair-raising time of it in those early days. Brunel's leadership was fast and furious in every direction, but he was always the kindliest of masters. To Gooch's dismay he and his quiet young north-country wife were expected to join in the whirl of fashionable social engagements that the Brunels so enjoyed, and as Hamilton Ellis has said: "The tremendous dinners of the period, the gay routs, the colossal balls, the elaborately gilded binges of late Georgian England shocked his north-country puritan soul to its depths." They were not exactly a good preparation for spending the rest of the night in the engine-sheds! Brunel spared himself neither in his work nor in the pursuit of his pleasures; but when things were urgent on the line duties came first, as on the memorable Christmas Day of 1838. The dissatisfaction felt with the performance of the early engines was expressed at top-level by Mr. G. H. Gibbs, one of the directors particularly concerned with locomotives. Brunel and Gooch carried out some experiments with the blast-pipe of the *North Star* to try and improve the steaming. An experimental run, to convince Mr. Gibbs of the efficacy of the new arrangements was fixed for December 29th; but at a late hour some unexpected difficulties were met. Although it was Christmas Day, Brunel and Gooch spent most of the day in the shops, though sparing time for a brief appearance at a hilarious party before returning to the recalcitrant *North Star*.

Their efforts were crowned with success, for Mr. Gibbs, who also kept a diary wrote on December 29th: "I went today to Maidenhead in an experimental train to test Brunel's statements as to the improvements effected in the *North Star*. We carried 43 tons of carriages and load at an average of 38 miles an hour, consuming only 0·95 lb. of coke per ton

of net weight per mile." In this short note a considerable
improvement in engine performance since the Rainhill days
is to be discerned, as the coke consumption of the *Rocket* on
her famous trials was 1·63 lb. per net ton mile. Nevertheless
the days were yet critical for Brunel, as well as Gooch, but
while coping with the harassing day-to-day problems of
running the trains Gooch was scheming out an engine of his
own design. Sturrock had not yet arrived from Scotland,
but working under Brunel's father was T. R. Crampton.
The younger Brunel soon discovered the possibilities latent
in this inventive young engineer, and he was transferred to
the Great Western staff to help Gooch in the design of the
new engines. The result was a milestone in locomotive
history. The *Firefly* arrived from the makers in March 1840,
just in time for the ceremonial opening of the line to Reading,
and when she covered the 36 miles back to Paddington in
45 minutes and attained 58 m.p.h. in the process it was
clear that the Great Western had an engine far superior to
anything which had so far been built.

The *Firefly*, while based upon the general layout of the
North Star was an entirely new design. This time nothing
was left to the discretion or fancy of individual manufacturers. Every detail was worked out between Gooch and
Crampton, to obviate all the weaknesses experienced with
the earlier engines and above all to ensure an ample supply
of steam. Great things were promised from the broad gauge;
speed was to be the watchword, and to sustain high speed
one must have a boiler that not only steams but will continue
to steam, hour after hour. The most noticeable external
difference between the *Firefly* and the *North Star* was in the
fire-box, which in the later engine took the form of a haystack rising high above the top of the boiler. The cylinders
on both engines were inside, and the wheel arrangement was
the 2-2-2—a single pair of driving wheels, with a pair of
carrying wheels fore and aft. In all, sixty-two engines of this
class were built, by various manufacturers, and they put the
Great Western motive power situation into a thoroughly
healthy state. The promise of great things on the broad
gauge was now in course of fulfilment, and the opening of
the Bristol and Exeter section of the line throughout on

May 1st, 1844, was signalised by the most spectacular locomotive performance the world had yet witnessed.

On that day not only was the special train from London to make the longest through journey ever yet attempted, 193¾ miles, but it was to be made by *one engine throughout*. In view of the difficulties that had been experienced in earlier years it might have seemed venturesome to attempt such a feat when all eyes would be upon the Great Western; but not only was it laid down that the through run would be made, but that it would be made at the amazing average speed of 39 m.p.h. The programme included for several stops on the way, to pick up distinguished guests, to take in water, and so on; so that the running average would need to be considerably higher. The engine chosen was naturally one of the "Firefly" class, the *Actæon*, and Daniel Gooch himself was the driver. With a load of six coaches they left Paddington at 7.30 a.m., and steamed triumphantly into Exeter on the stroke of 12.30 p.m. Then, as if that were not enough for one day, the return special left Exeter at 5.20 p.m. with the same engine, and just to show what *could* be done Gooch knocked twenty minutes off the schedule, and brought the train into Paddington at 10 p.m. Afterwards Gooch wrote in his diary:

It was a hard day's work for me, as apart from driving the engine 387 miles, I had to be out early in the morning to see that all was right for the trip, and while at Exeter was busy with matters connected with the opening, so that my only chance of sitting down was for the hour we were at dinner. Next day my back ached so that I could hardly walk. Mr. Brunel wrote me a very handsome letter, thanking me for all I had done, and all were very much pleased.

Well they might be pleased! It was indeed the long-hoped-for day of triumph for the broad gauge, but it was a triumph that merely helped to force the issue in the growing controversy and concern over the existence of the two different gauges on railways in this country. In contrast to the Great Western policy of developing high-speed services and generally forcing the pace, on the narrow gauge even the trunk routes such as the London and Birmingham and the

Grand Junction were inclined to be content with much more modest progress, and the locomotives were the smallest that would do the existing job. For some time after its opening the London and Birmingham Railway was worked by little four-wheeled engines of Edward Bury's make weighing no more than $12\frac{1}{4}$ tons; engines of this type were being built new as late as 1845, whereas Gooch's "Firefly" class weighed 24 tons without their tenders. The champions of the narrow gauge were to be found in the north-eastern counties, and by the year 1845 there were some fine engines at work on the lines ultimately amalgamated to form the North Eastern Railway. Robert Stephenson was experimenting with the earliest of his "long-boilered" type, while the *Richmond*, a 2–2–2 express engine of the Great North of England Railway built by Hawthorn's, was to figure prominently before the gauge trials.

The Stephenson long-boilered type deserves more than a passing mention, for although it had a relatively short life in express passenger service it became, with suitable adaptation the standard type for heavy freight service on the Stockton and Darlington Railway; examples, indeed, remained in regular service until 1923! The original idea behind the introduction of the long boiler was quite different. In the Rainhill days the problem had been to make locomotives steam; but the sharpening of the blast, while achieving that object had resulted in a great deal of unburnt fuel and heat being ejected from the chimney, and in an attempt to harness that source of power Stephenson lengthened his boilers. In the *Prince of Wales*, a 2–2–2 engine delivered to the York and North Midland Railway in 1842, the length of the boiler barrel was no less than 14 ft., in contrast to the 9 ft. of Gooch's *Firefly*. Stephenson patented the arrangement, but the very feature he patented made the engines more difficult to steam. The draught on the fire had to be created through a much longer length of boiler flue tube, and unless the blast was sharpened still further there would be insufficient draught to secure rapid combustion in the firebox. Sharpening the blast, on the other hand, restricts the flow of exhaust steam, and the restriction can easily be enough to set quite a low limit on the maximum speed of the engine. So it is not surprising that express engines fitted with the patent long boiler did not last very long in service.

For freight service on a line like the Stockton and Darlington the long boiler was ideal. The coal trains never got any long stretches of unchecked running. Time was spent in sidings waiting for "line clear", and the speeds were slow. The long boiler provided a large reservoir full of steam, ready for use when required; the fire-box was small, and therefore used the minimum amount of coal when the engine was standing. Plenty of steam was ready for a big effort when starting away, and if pressure was dropped when the train was on the run the next check, or stop would not be long in coming and then the situation could be readily restored. On an express train, with a run of 40 or 50 miles between stations this could not be done. Quite apart from any technical considerations the long-boilered express engines built by Stephenson's were a mis-shapen awkward-looking lot, in contrast to the simple, straightforward standard design of Hawthorns. The *Richmond* was a powerful engine—on paper at any rate; but there is more than a suggestion that the original cylinders were bigger than the boiler could cope with. After a mishap, which called for some rebuilding of the engine in 1849 the cylinders were considerably reduced in size.

The long-boilered engines had another claim to distinction; one of them built for the York and North Midland Railway was the first to have the world-famous "link motion" for operating the valves. Until 1842 reversing mechanisms had been relatively crude and cumbersome affairs. Some engineers use the so-called "gab" motion in which there were two huge V-shaped members or "gabs", one for forward running and one for reverse; the driver engaged the reversing rod actuating lever into one or other of the V's, which in turn were oscillated backwards and forwards by the motion of eccentrics on the driving axle of the locomotive. This oscillation was transmitted through the gabs to the valve spindle and the valves were opened and closed as required. There was a simpler mechanism that needed two levers to operate it; one to de-clutch, so to speak, and another to effect the actual reversal. The trouble with this device was that the two levers on the engine footplate were oscillating backwards and forwards while the engine was in motion, and as such were a great nuisance to the driver. Then, in 1842, William Howe, foreman pattern maker at the Forth Street works, connected the rods from the forward and reverse eccentrics to either ends of a single curved link. This link had a central slot in which could be slid, upwards and downwards as required a die block to which the valve spindle was connected by links. Compared with all that had gone before this "curved link" motion was simplicity itself as a reversing gear; for forward gear the die block was moved to the top of the slot in the link, and it was removed to the bottom for reverse.

It may well be that William Howe had no other object in mind when he made a wooden model, and showed it to Mr. Hutchieson, who was then Works Manager at Forth Street. Hutchieson on the other hand realised at once that here, not only was there a very neat and simple reversing gear, but the fact that the die-clock moved some distance in the slot of the curved link between full forward and full reverse positions gave the possibility of intermediate adjustments. The steam supply to the cylinders could be cut off earlier in the piston stroke when running fast, and the expensive properties of the steam used to the fullest advantage. Several earlier valve motions had provided for expansive working, but by complicated and somewhat ineffectual mechanisms. Robert Stephenson was in London at the time, and so Hutchieson sent the model to him. Stephenson was delighted, for he saw clearly the great possibilities of such a gear, and instructions were sent to Newcastle to apply it at once to one of two locomotives then building for the York and North Midland Railway. Howe received a present of twenty guineas from the firm, and received reward from the firm four years later when he was appointed engineer to the Stephenson group of collieries in the Chesterfield district. Strictly speaking the curved link motion should be called the Howe-Stephenson; but for upwards of a hundred years now it has been known as the Stephenson Link Motion. It is still widely used today, though the fashion is now to employ the somewhat later radial gear invented in 1844 by Egide Walschaerts, a shop foreman in Brussels on the Belgian State

Railway. The Howe-Stephenson gear is used most extensively today on the locomotives of the former Great Western
Railway, and in the autumn of 1954 a mixed traffic engine
so fitted, the *Fountains Hall*, ran the high-speed Bristolian
express in emergency, covering the last $77\frac{1}{4}$ miles of the
journey, from Swindon into Paddington in 58 *minutes*—an
average speed of almost 80 m.p.h. This run was a wonderful
present-day tribute to the working efficiency of the link
motion.

But the steam locomotive was scarcely launched on to the
new main-line railways in this country before inventors were
thinking of still newer forms of motive power. Although
steam locomotives of the "thirties" and "forties" used coke
it was not always possible to consume all the smoke, and the
prevalence of open carriages made smoke, no less than rain,
sleet and snow a highly objectionable accompaniment of
travel. In 1839, there was patented, jointly by Mr. Samuel
Clegg and Messrs. Jacob and Joseph Samuda, the "Atmospheric" system of propulsion. It was another attempt to
eliminate the self-contained locomotive and provide the
power necessary for traction from stationary engine houses
spaced at intervals along the line. But whereas earlier
exponents of stationary engines had based their proposals
upon cable traction, with all the attendant inconveniences
of changing from one cable to another as successive engine
houses were reached, the "Atmospheric" provided a continuous source of power supply all along the line. It was in
one way analogous to electric traction, wherein power is
collected from a continuous conductor rail, or overhead line.
In the "Atmospheric" a cast-iron tube was laid between the
rails, and the stationary engines exhausted air from the tube.
The motor carriage of a train had depending from it a piston
which fitted closely in the tube. Along the top of the tube
was a slit about $2\frac{1}{2}$ in. wide; this slit was closed by a flap
of leather which was secured to the tube at one side of the
slit. One edge of the leather thus formed a continuous hinge.
The air was exhausted from the tube in front of the train,
and the suction created on the piston drew the train along;
the bar carrying the piston pushed the leather flap aside,
and it resealed immediately afterwards.

Quite apart from the amenities of travel resulting from having no locomotive the system had the advantage that greater power could be made available for haulage on heavy gradients by having more stationary engines and a larger tube. Due to the limited tractive power of the early locomotives the first main lines were constructed with very slight gradients. In hilly country the cost of the great earthworks was tremendous, as I have told in connection with Blisworth Cutting, Kilsby Tunnel, and other monumental works. But the "Atmospheric" held out prospects of much cheaper constructional costs, since railways might then follow the lie of the land more closely. It was first tried on a short stretch of line across Wormwood Scrubs—part of the present West London line connecting Willesden and Clapham Junctions. That was in 1840. The Board of Trade ordered an enquiry into its working, since it was proposed for the Dalkey branch of the Dublin and Kingstown Railway. The enquiry was conducted by Sir Frederick Smith and Professor Barlow, and their report was so favourable that it was not only adopted for the Dalkey Line, but also for the Croydon Railway on the advice of the engineer for that project, William Cubitt (61). Almost alone among the great engineers of the day Robert Stephenson stood out against it. Despite the arguments about cheapness in construction of the line Stephenson considered that in operation it would be more costly than locomotives, and he had some difficulty in persuading the directors of the Chester and Holyhead Railway, then under construction, that the latest mode of railway travel was not really suitable.

It is easy to see now what a hopelessly impracticable arrangement it was. Even if it had proved possible to keep the mechanism itself in good repair the system would have been quite inflexible. The power that could be exerted to haul a train along was always constant; extra power could not be obtained for working a specially heavy, or fast service, and although he did not stress the point at the time Robert Stephenson may have had this in mind. Nevertheless the Croydon Railway was built as an "Atmospheric", but what gave the system its greatest fillip was when Brunel recommended its use for the South Devon Railway from Exeter to

Plymouth (54, 55). Brunel's name alone carried tremendous weight. The Great Western had rallied from the early set-backs; the "Firefly" class engines were running, and the through service to Exeter had been inaugurated with the spectacular runs of the *Actæon*. In a long report to the directors of the South Devon Railway, in August 1844, interspersed with much playful sarcasm there occurs their passage:

> I must assume that as a means of applying stationary power the Atmospheric System has been successful, and that, unless where under some very peculiar circumstances it is inapplicable, it is a good economical mode of applying stationary power.
> I am aware that this opinion is directly opposed to that of Mr. Robert Stephenson, who has written and published an elaborate statement of experiments and calculations founded upon them, the results of which support his opinion.
> It does not seem to me that we can obtain the minute data required for the mathematical investigation of such a question, and that such calculations, dependent as they are upon an unattained precision in experiments, are as likely to lead you very far from the truth as not.
> By the same mode M. Mallet and other French engineers have proved the success of the system; and by the same mode of investigation Dr. Lardner arrived at all those results regarding steam navigation and the speed to be attained on railways, which have since proved so erroneous. . . .

One can well imagine Brunel's delight at having an oppor-tunity to "debunk" at least one so-called scientist; for in those early days no man, under the cloak of "science", talked or wrote more rubbish about railways than Dr. Dionysius Lardner!

And so Brunel received authority to go ahead with the "Atmospheric" on the South Devon line. Of the civil engi-neering features of that beautiful railway I have more to say in the next chapter, but it was perhaps fortunate that the inherent weaknesses of the "Atmospheric" system were revealed before matters had gone too far. By this time Vignoles had also joined the courageous band of engineers who supported the "Atmospheric", though the cause was weakened sadly in this same year of 1844 when Jacob Samuda was killed. Vignoles thought that if Samuda had been spared he might have found a way round the difficulties that came to beset Brunel. These difficulties were of a most prosaic kind, yet they proved insuperable. The leather flap proved highly susceptible to changes in the weather. At times it became saturated with moisture, and at others it was shrivelled up with the heat and failed to seal the pipe. In very cold weather freezing took place, but the most serious results came when the leather began to tear right away from its mountings. In a report to the directors dated August 1848, Brunel gives a long and detailed explanation of his troubles, but he does not include the factor that probably accentuated all other causes of failure, the effect of the salt in the sea air on the coastal secton from Exeter to Newton Abbot; and to add insult to injury the destruction of the leather was in many places completed by rats!

Brunel had to confess himself beaten, and in the report previously mentioned he wrote: "From the foregoing observations, it will be evident that I cannot consider the result of our experience of the working between Exeter and Newton such as to induce one to recommend the extension of the system." But despite the heavy costs that had already been incurred, which were as much due to the deficiencies of the pumping engines as to leakage from deterioration of the leather flap valve, there were some who urged the continuance of the experiment. In changing over to steam locomotive haulage in September 1848 the directors offered the use of their atmospheric equipment for further tests, while the Chairman of the Board, Mr. Thomas Gill, dissociated himself from the general decision to abandon atmospheric haulage, even temporarily as it might prove, and presented to the shareholders a strongly worded memorandum urging its immediate resumption. Some of the leading engineers of the day were equally disappointed by the South Devon decision. Vignoles looked forward to an eventual solution of the difficulties, and John Rennie in the airy style of his autobiography writes:

My brother and myself were much taken with this system, and made several of the steam engines for it, that answered their purpose perfectly, and we thought that by a little more

perseverance in it, the difficulties complained of might have
been overcome, but the proprietors would not listen either to
Brunel or ourselves. The Stephensons made a dead set against
it, and taking the facts at the time, perhaps they were right;
but it is very rarely that a new invention succeeds at the first
or second trial; it required time to ascertain the defects, and
to study more minutely the remedy, and, after a little while,
the cure for the evil is found out.

Actually the pumping engines were very far from satisfactory. Some were certainly supplied by the Rennies, some
came from Mandsley's and some from no less a firm than
Boulton and Watt. But John Rennie's reference to them is
characteristic of many passages in his autobiography, written
in the evening of his life when he was basking in the glory
of a knighthood; events back in the high-noon of his life
were apt to be seen through rose-coloured glasses! Furthermore Brunel did nothing more to urge the continuance of
the system. Far from it! His great qualities were never
shown to finer effect than at times of adversity, and when
he was confronted with the constant practical difficulties of
the scheme he had recommended, he was the first to counsel
abandonment. His personal pride might have been encouraged to try again when Thomas Gill made such a
determined stand in favour of the "Atmospheric"; but he
stood by his earlier recommendation to abandon it, with a
simple disregard of every consideration except the interests
of those by whom he was employed. Although at the time
men like Vignoles, Cubitt, and the Rennies were arrayed in
his support Brunel took the failure of the South Devon very
much to heart, and although he remained engineer to the
company and built the rest of the line he refused to accept
any remuneration for his services beyond a nominal retaining
fee, from the date of the abandonment of the Atmospheric
System.

William Cubitt installed it on the London and Croydon
Railway, but there it dropped out of use with far less
publicity than in Brunel's case, and the recollections of it
are amusing rather than poignant. C. F. Dendy-Marshall
quotes a contemporary newspaper comment made when the
line was in course of construction:

Considerable apprehension has been entertained by lovers of the sweet rusticity of English landscape, lest the stations on lines of Atmospheric Railway should destroy the picturesque character of the inland districts, by giving them the chimneyed aspect so singularly indicative of manufacturing localities. It appears, that for the purpose of blowing off the air withdrawn from the atmospheric tubes, and discharging the surplus steam from the powerful engines to be used in effecting the exhaustion, tall chimneys, or "stacks" as they are technically called, will be necessary at the stations. These would of course be very unsightly objects, and as such are justly objected to by all persons of taste, to say nothing of the gentry who might be favoured with one or more within sight of their park walks or drawing-room windows. To get over this difficulty, it has been determined by the architects of the Croydon and Epsom line to give their chimneys an architectural character, and to relieve their baldness by the addition of proportions and decorations which have hitherto belonged almost exclusively to the bell towers of the early Gothic churches. And, as in the opinion of the promoters of this scheme, beauty is as cheap as deformity, they have taken another step in the right direction by a resolution to construct the station and engine houses in the style of the half-timbered manor houses of the middle ages.

The stations were named after neighbouring inns, so that one found delightful places such as "Dartmouth Arms" and "Jolly Sailor" on the run from London Bridge to Croydon. It does, perhaps, spoil the illusion of being deep in the heart of the English countryside to add that the present names of these two stations are Forest Hill and Norwood Junction! Day tickets with complete break-of-journey facilities were issued so that passengers could visit the beautiful country served by the line, and from an advertisement we read that "Marquees are erected in the wood close to the Anerley station and parties using the railway will be permitted to angle in the adjacent canal, which abounds in fish"!

But I am digressing far from locomotives and locomotive men, and I must return to the year 1845 when the Gauge Commission was sitting. And what a scene the hearing of those witnesses must sometimes have presented! Reading through the cold, formal minutes of the proceedings one can detect, even at this lapse of time, that feelings ran high, and a few sharp flashes of criticism, of satirical humour, and of scorn are preserved in the published records. Brunel, who was then at the very height of his professional activities, clearly grudged the time necessary to prepare his evidence and appear before the Commissioners, and as much as told them so! It is generally thought that the men of the Great Western stood alone in their backing of a wider gauge. This is very far from the truth. The Stephenson "group", Locke, Nicholas Wood, and Robert Stephenson himself stood fast by the 4 ft. 8½ in. gauge, taking it as one of those items to be accepted without question, and to be defended through thick and thin. But Vignoles, William Cubitt, and John Braithwaite all expressed strong views that a larger gauge would have been preferable. Vignoles advocated 6 ft., while Braithwaite built the Eastern Counties line on a gauge of 5 ft.

The Great Western men throughout based their advocacy of the 7 ft. gauge on the superior service that was possible, and on the higher speeds that could be safely attained. It must have been a little disconcerting to them to hear first Stephenson and then Locke argue against high speed. They both considered 40 m.p.h. was quite fast enough. The Commissioners pressed Locke on the subject of speeds run on the Grand Junction and the South Western asking:

"In point of fact, can you now attain as high a velocity for the express trains on the Grand Junction as is obtained on the Great Western?"

Locke replied: "In answering that question I may say that I do not exactly know what velocity could be obtained upon the Great Western, not having experience as to that line; but I have no doubt that we could, if it were safe, run our express trains upon either lines at 50 m.p.h.; they now travel 40 m.p.h. Our time to Southampton is two hours and it is 78 miles, very nearly 40 m.p.h. including stoppages, and I am quite sure that if it were a matter of necessity we could travel at 50 m.p.h."

"Do you think", the Commissioner then asked, "the state of the road would admit of your travelling at that speed with safety?"

"I do not", Locke answered. "I am very much opposed to it; I do not think it is safe."

35   A Beattie express locomotive, London and South
Western Railway (1859 class)

36   Broad gauge express locomotive, Bristol and Exeter Railway.
Note "policeman" at extreme left

37   Daniel Gooch, with a model of one of his "Firefly" class locomotives

From a photograph taken in 1845

Daniel Gooch when his turn came, "cashed in" well and truly on the subject of unsafe running at speed on the 4 ft. 8½ in. gauge (37). He was in the fortunate position of having ridden on some of the rival engines, including the *White Horse of Kent*. This latter was one of Stephenson's "long boiler" type. "The day I was on", Gooch remarked, "she had been running about 18,000 miles, and she was in such a state then that she was not safe." In a later stage in the hearing of evidence Stephenson's great friend, G. P. Bidder, took up this point, and blamed the South Eastern Railway for the state of the *White Horse of Kent*: "She was the only engine adequate to her duty they had at that time, and they fairly ran her off her legs; they never blew her boiler out, or took any care of her whatever, and therefore it was comparing an engine literally worn out with a first-rate engine, consequently the conclusion, in my opinion, is fallacious." Nevertheless, the *White Horse of Kent* was a bit of a terror. In his diaries David Joy remarks of the long-boilered engines: "These all had six wheels under the boiler. The most notorious of them, the *White Horse of Kent*, signalised herself by going off the road repeatedly and killing a man or two.

"This engine, with about 12 ft. boiler, all wheels under it, and cylinders outside, further curtailing the wheel base, and adding to the overhanging and disturbing weight, was a notorious roller, although just now rose the cry for a low centre of gravity to get steadiness."

Claims and counter claims continued, but as the enquiry proceeded it was clear that the weight of evidence was turning against the Great Western, not so much on the score of performance but of practical politics. Although Cubitt and Vignoles had spoken in favour of a *wider* gauge than 4 ft. 8½ in. they themselves had built narrow gauge lines out of expediency; and men like Sir J. Willoughby Gordon, the Quartermaster General of the Army, supported the narrow gauge simply because there was already a far greater mileage laid, and that he viewed with some concern the inconveniences of changing trains from broad to narrow gauge when moving troops. George Hudson, in the flood-tide of his railway career, spoke with his usual "brag and bounce":

8

"We have", he said, "on the York and North Midland, carried from 700 to 800 tons with one engine." Hudson's first name might well have been Ananias!

It was natural to find a man of Nicholas Wood's practical, precise and orderly mind backing the *status quo* in the North of England. Prior to the opening of the enquiry he ran one of the latest Hawthorn 2–2–2 engines from Darlington to York, 44 miles in 47 minutes, with a load of two small coaches, and while he admitted in his evidence that he had travelled at 64 m.p.h. on the Great Western, he considered that 60 m.p.h. was "too high a rate for convenience or continued safety; 45 miles an hour is as high a rate as I should say ought to be practised, and at 45 miles an hour I have no hesitation in saying that I think the narrow gauge is quite as safe as the other".

The Commissioners pressed him on the subject of speed generally, and the possibility of the alternative gauges for still higher speeds. In reading the questions and answers one cannot fail to be struck by the farsightedness of Sir Frederic Smith, who conducted the enquiry, and of his assessors—George Airy, the Astronomer Royal, and Peter Barlow. With the exception of Brunel and Gooch, the engineers called upon to give evidence were clearly looking no further forward than their immediate problems of the day. Railway speed had gone forward in such style that one feels that men like Robert Stephenson and Locke were inclined to stay the hand of further development and consolidate the position, whereas to Brunel and Gooch there was clearly no limit on the horizon! The Commissioners were evidently concerned over the possibility of still higher speeds, and in pursuing the possibility with a man of Wood's technical ability and scientific outlook they were evidently seeking to find out if with higher speeds the broad gauge might offer such advantages as to suggest its general adoption for the future. Wood in his evidence endeavoured to keep things on the plane of practical politics and said: "I think it would not be consistent with prudence to found a system upon an imaginary rate of speed; I think that 60 miles an hour is the utmost limit that we ought to speculate upon. Above that rate of speed is beyond the limit of judicious travelling."

"And up to that", the Commissioner continued, "you think there is no remarkable difference?"

"Up to that, I think, there is no difference between the two gauges."

"But", continued the questioners, "if any desperate man should want to run at 100 miles an hour, you would recommend him to take the wide gauge?"

"Of course, he is more likely to accomplish his object by the wide gauge than the narrow."

This was a point; and one of the Commissioners jumped in eagerly in following up: "But not with greater safety?"

At this Wood exploded: "Not with greater safety; I think he is as liable to break his neck on the broad gauge, as on the other!"

Towards the end of this lengthy enquiry, which had lasted from August 6th, 1845, until late in November, Brunel was recalled, and suggested that definite running trials should be made under the eyes of the Commissioners between selected broad gauge and narrow gauge locomotives. This was the last thing the narrow gauge people wanted! But the Commission was interested, and on December 2nd with Bidder representing the narrow gauge parties the conditions of test were argued out with Brunel. The narrow gauge could not compete for length of run with the best the Great Western could do. Brunel proposed to run to Exeter and back from Paddington; but no comparable conditions could be found, or indeed could have been operated, and eventually the trial resolved itself into the broad gauge running between Paddington and Didcot, 53 miles, while the narrow gauge trials were made between York and Darlington, 44 miles. Four return trips were made, with loads of 50, 60, 70 and 80 tons, and in these tests one of Gooch's 7 ft. 2–2–2 engines, the *Ixion*, was pitted against the latest Stephenson long-boiler creation, *The Great A*. One feels that there were far better engines running than *The Great A*; but she was new from the shops at the time and was the chosen representative. In any event the result of the trials was what the moderns would call "a push-over", in that the *Ixion* did by far the finer work. It was indeed a resounding personal triumph for Gooch.

8*

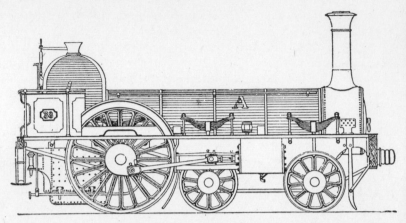

38   Stephenson's *Great A*

While the decision of the Gauge Commissioners in favour of the 4 ft. 8½ in. gauge was almost a foregone conclusion, in view of its preponderance in the country, handsome tributes were paid to the Great Western on two points:

"We feel it our duty to observe that the public are mainly indebted for the present rate of speed, and the increased accommodation of railway carriages to the genius of Mr. Brunel and the liberality of the Great Western Railway.

And again, in regard to the locomotive trials:

"We consider them as confirming the statement and results given by Mr. Gouch, in his evidence, proving, as they do, that the broad gauge engines possess greater capabilities for speed with equal loads, and generally speaking, of propelling greater loads with equal speed; and moreover, that the working of such engines is economical where very high speeds are required, or where loads to be conveyed are such as to require the full power of the engine."

Admirable though the broad gauge was for fast running with main-line express trains, such trains form a relatively small proportion of the total traffic in this country, and seen in retrospect the decision to standardise on 4 ft. 8½ in. was unquestionably the best for railways as a whole. The broad gauge would have been a great nuisance on sharply-curved mineral lines, in collieries and places where space is confined,

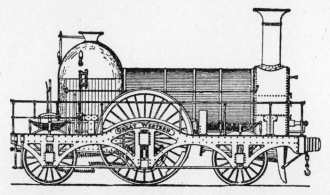

39   The *Great Western*: Gooch's "colossal" locomotive

not to mention the additional width that would have been needed for marshalling yards, and other concentration points, the eventual size of which was barely dreamed of in 1845.

In anticipation of the prolonging of the dispute, however, the Great Western directors were clearly out to stop at nothing, and early in 1846 Gooch was instructed to build "a colossal locomotive working with all speed". One can well imagine how that brilliant young pair, Gooch and Sturrock revelled in such an instruction, and "with all speed" they went indeed. It was the first engine to be built entirely at Swindon works, and the records show that the design and construction took only thirteen weeks; while Gooch burned vast quantities of midnight oil on the design, Sturrock had the shops going night and day, and the "colossal locomotive" was steamed on April 1st, 1846(39). Colossal she was for those days, though in design and appearance no more than an enlarged edition of the "Firefly" class; but in going far in advance of any locomotive so far put on the rails, Gooch set himself some major problems. The boiler was built to carry the high working pressure of 100 lb. per sq. in. while the huge "haystack" fire-box was made almost entirely by hand hammering. There had been no time for any very elaborate drawings; pen and ink dimensioned sketches were sent round to the various shops. During constructional days she became known in the works as the "Lightning"; but her name eventually was the *Great Western*.

The *Ixion* had done well enough in the gauge trials, but the *Great Western* immediately set some entirely new standards of running. She took a load of 100 tons from Paddington to Swindon at an average speed of 59 m.p.h., and on another occasion with a load of 140 tons she averaged 55 m.p.h. These were remarkable runs, seeing that the line is on a very gradual rise all the way. An even more spectacular performance was put up on June 1st, 1846, when the *Great Western* hauled the Paddington–Exeter crack express in both directions; this distance is 194 miles each way, and deducting the time of station stops the time while on the run was 208 minutes going down, and 211 minutes up, giving the extraordinary average speeds of 54½ and 53 m.p.h. While, no doubt, a special effort was made on this occasion it was enough to show what could be done on the broad gauge as early as the year 1846. Less than seventeen years had elapsed since Rainhill; George Stephenson was still alive, and recalling his great concept of railways covering the land one can, perhaps, imagine his hearing of the exploit with slightly mixed feelings wishing that the engine to achieve such honour had been designed by his own son, instead of this redoubtable youngster Daniel Gooch. On the other hand he might, like his friend and former chief Nicholas Wood, have felt that the Great Western was forcing the pace too much. There is an amusing story of an encounter he had with Brunel when the Newcastle and Berwick Railway was being projected. At one time there was a suggestion that it might be built on the "Atmospheric" principle. Brunel travelled to Newcastle to sound local opinion; while there he met George Stephenson, who immediately, and with mock ferocity seized him by the collar and demanded to know what he was doing north of the Tyne! Actually, however, one of the happiest features of railway engineering history in those years was that despite their opposition on the subject of the gauges Robert Stephenson and Brunel became the closest of personal friends.

The last witness to give evidence before the Gauge Commission was Major-General C. W. Pasley, an Inspecting Officer of the Board of Trade. As an impartial observer his criticism of the Stephenson long-boilered engines carries far

more weight than the allegations made by Gooch, or of the
defence put up by Bidder. General Pasley attributed their
bad riding partly to the disposition of the wheels, and
partly to the fact that the moving parts were not balanced.
He thought the *White Horse of Kent* would be definitely
unsafe at more than about 50 m.p.h. Some confirmation
of this risk came about twenty years later with another
engine of the long-boilered type, on the Shrewsbury and
Chester line. This old engine, built by Longridge in 1846,
was put on to assist a heavy excursion train; near Rednal,
where the speed was high the long-boilered engine, which
was leading, left the road, and in the ensuing pile-up many
were killed. But of equal significance in General Pasley's
evidence are his references to certain rebuildings of locomotives carried out on the Grand Junction Railway. Here
Joseph Locke was engineer-in-chief, and W. B. Buddicom
was locomotive superintendent, and to join them in 1840
had come Alexander Allan. The Grand Junction then had
some sixty engines, nearly all with the cylinders inside; the
driving axles had to be cranked for attachment of the
connecting rods, and this constituted a point of weakness.
With the methods of manufacture then available it was
becoming a difficult task to make these cranked axles sound
enough to transmit the power of the larger engines, and on
the Grand Junction especially the stresses set up when
rounding the sharp curve at Newton-le-Willows, where the
line from the south joined the old Liverpool and Manchester
Railway, caused fractures of crank axles to occur with
alarming frequency.

To obviate this serious trouble Allan, as works manager,
suggested a form of rebuilding to be applied to the 2–2–2
engines in service. The cylinders were to be moved outside,
which would enable plain crank axles to be used, and the
cylinders themselves placed between the inside and outside
frame plates, making a very snug and solid attachment. At
that time in locomotive development the frames were more
often than not a collection of "bits and pieces"; racking
stresses were set up when the engine was working, attach-
ments worked loose, and failures occurred. Allan, however,
put forward a thoroughly sound frame design, and his

proposal for rebuilding one or two of the older engines was accepted by Buddicom and Joseph Locke. It proved most successful, and engines to this standard design were built at Crewe for the London and North Western Railway down to the year 1858. They could be recognised anywhere by the shape of the outside framing at the front end, where the plate was splayed out to accommodate a long slot for access to the crosshead. Robert Sinclair took the same design into Scotland, though the manner of its introduction there came in rather a roundabout way. For a short time Sinclair was on the Grand Junction with Buddicom. Now when Locke became engineer of the Paris and Rouen Railway, Buddicom saw an opportunity. With William Allcard, who had been one of George Stephenson's assistants in the construction of the Liverpool and Manchester Railway, he set up a locomotive manufacturing business in France, and Robert Sinclair was appointed manager of the works at Les Chartereux. There the famous Buddicom engines were built, based on the principles adopted in Alexander Allan's Grand Junction rebuilds. One beautiful example long since retired from active service, was brought over from France to occupy a place of honour in the Festival of Britain Exhibition in London in 1951. In the meantime Joseph Locke was building the Caledonian Railway, and in 1848 Sinclair was made locomotive superintendent; thenceforward the Allan type of engine became standard on one of the largest groups of lines in Scotland.

The "Allans" were small engines. Even the new ones built at Crewe from 1845 onwards were little mites of $19\frac{1}{2}$ tons total weight, compared with Gooch's *colossi* on the Great Western. And the group of lines principally associated with the Stephenson "school"—the London and Birmingham, the Grand Junction, and the Caledonian—became identified with what is sometimes called the "small-engine" policy. The engines were just big enough for the existing traffic, and no more. In addition, the aim of the managements concerned was to work the trains with the minimum of expenditure; speed was a secondary consideration, and for many years the London and North Western recognised an average of 40 m.p.h. as the hall-mark of a first-class express train. With the growth of traffic it was foreseen that speed might become an embarrassment, and where a virtual monopoly existed, as with the services from Euston to Birmingham, Liverpool and Glasgow the spur of competition was absent.

It was at about the same time as the Gauge Commission was in session that something of a sensation occurred in British engineering circles. Robert Stephenson had been admitted as a Member of the Institution of Civil Engineers in 1830, during Telford's long tenure of the Presidency; but with the spread of railways more and more men came forward as railway engineers, and those practising in other branches of the profession felt that as things were going they would ultimately be swamped by the railway men. Furthermore the Railway Mania was working up to its full height; many spurious and impracticable schemes were afoot, and each of these, before presentation to Parliament must necessarily be sponsored by an "engineer". The experienced men were overwhelmed with genuine projects, but many others with less regard for professional etiquette or reputation styled themselves "engineers", and sought membership of the Institution to substantiate their claim. The Institution of Civil Engineers was fully alive to the danger of admitting unqualified men, and so each new applicant had to submit a thesis as proof of his capabilities. This very essential precaution was introduced at an exceptional time; but just at that very time George Stephenson expressed a desire to join the Institution. He was already taking an active part in the work of the Mechanics' Institutes established in many northern towns, and no doubt wished to join in the higher councils of engineers. In the year 1846 the achievements of George Stephenson were not merely known throughout the engineering profession, but with the Mania still in full blast they were on everyone's lips. If ever there was a case for discrimination it was there, in George Stephenson's application to join the "Civils". It was unfortunate, however, that John Rennie was President at the time, and whereas a "bigger" man would have used his influence to make an exception to their newly-formed rule Rennie apparently allowed the "letter of the law" to be invoked, with the result

that Stephenson of all men was asked to submit a proba-
tionary essay as proof of his capacity as an engineer!
Naturally he refused to accept such humiliating conditions,
and the action of the Institution of Civil Engineers, when it
became known caused astonishment and indignation throughout the railway engineering world.

The affair became the topic of conversation in a hut at
the lineside of the Birmingham and Gloucester Railway one
day in 1846, when a small group of engineers was sheltering
from a heavy rainstorm during some locomotive trials. A
suggestion was made that mechanical engineers might have
a separate institution of their own. How the Institution of
Mechanical Engineers came into being as a result of that lineside discussion is a fascinating story in itself, but here we are
concerned particularly with the moving spirit, James Edward
McConnell. At that time he was locomotive superintendent
of the Birmingham and Gloucester Railway, and the first
discussions about the new Institution took place at his own
home in Bromsgrove. In July 1846, however, McConnell
became locomotive engineer of the Southern Division of the
newly-formed London and North Western Railway, and he
had already taken up the reins in this important post when,
in October 1846, he took the chair at what proved to be the
first meeting of the Institution of Mechanical Engineers.
Very soon afterwards George Stephenson was offered and
accepted the Presidency of the new Institution.

David Joy recording in his diary the bad riding of the
Stephenson long-boilered type express engines added:
". . . just now rose the cry for a low centre-of-gravity to get
steadiness". The behaviour of locomotives as vehicles was
then but slightly understood, and it was Crampton who made
a determined break with convention when, in 1843, he
patented a locomotive design in which the driving axle was
abaft the boiler back-plate. By this means he could mount
a large boiler without the necessity of pitching it high to
clear the driving axles. It was hoped that the low centre-
of-gravity would give that steadiness in running that the
Stephenson types lacked, while the large boiler would provide
ample steam for long non-stop runs in the Great Western
style. Crampton took out his patent while still on the

G.W.R., but in the following year he took a post under John Rennie, and the wider sphere of activity connected with a consultant's office enabled Crampton to interest certain foreign administrations in his patent locomotive. So it befell that the first Crampton locomotive, with its huge pair of driving wheels at the rear end, was built in Whitehaven, by Messrs. Tulk and Ley, to the order of the Namur and Liége Railway in Belgium. But though some highly picturesque examples of the type were put to work on various lines in Britain they never "caught on" here. In France and Germany they did remarkably well, and I can repeat again the French expression, *"prendre le Crampton"*, which meant nothing more nor less than going by train. Cramptons were then synonymous with railway travel!

In England J. E. McConnell was making short work of the small-engine tradition on the London and Birmingham line. He tried some "Cramptons", including the very large eight-wheeled engine *Liverpool*; but their work taken all round, was disappointing. A number of fine individual runs were made; they were fast, and could pull heavy loads, but contrary to expectations their riding was harsh and uncomfortable, and they had a bad effect upon the track. After his trial of the "Cramptons" McConnell set about designing his own engines. It was unfortunate in a way that he was not on the scene earlier, or the Great Western would have had a much harder run for their money in the gauge trials of 1846. His 2–2–2 express engines of 1851, with their 7-ft. driving wheels and large boilers were splendid examples of locomotive construction at that time; moreover, to quote David Joy: "they rode like a swing". The spacing of the wheels, the springing, the weight distribution, and the extent to which the revolving and reciprocating parts are balanced, all contribute to the riding qualities, and in his 1851 engines —the "Bloomers", as they were nicknamed—McConnell achieved almost ideal proportions. In these engines it was demonstrated that large boilers carried in the conventional position were not incompatable with good riding; such rolling movement as there was when running took the form of a gentle swaying that had no ill effects upon the track. Hawthorn's produced some similar engines of comparable quality, while E. B. Wilson and Co. of Leeds began building their "Jenny Linds", in the same tradition.

In 1850 Archibald Sturrock left the Great Western. It was inevitable that a man of his ability and drive should seek an independent command, and so at the age of thirty-four, armed with a glowing letter of commendation from Brunel, he applied for the post of Locomotive Superintendent of the Great Northern Railway. He was duly appointed, at a salary of £500 per annum, and one chuckles over the immediate sequel; for having arrived on the Great Northern he was asked to recommend someone as carriage and wagon superintendent. Of course he could! He proposed himself, *and* got the job, thereby adding another £250 a year to his salary. Did I say earlier that Sturrock was a "go-getter"? Some years later the Great Western were to be reminded of this, verily, in letters of fire! Although it is taking the story forward some thirteen years it is worth the digression to show Sturrock's indomitable character. This new "battle of gauges" took place within the grimy precincts of what is now the Inner Circle. This first length of the Metropolitan line from Paddington to Farringdon Street had been opened in 1863. It was laid with the mixed gauge, so that broad gauge trains could run through. At first the Great Western worked all the trains, and that company rather looked upon the Metropolitan as their own property; so that when the Great Northern were about to institute a service of their own, using the connecting tunnels to the "Inner Circle" line at Kings Cross with, it should be added, the full approval of the Metropolitan management, the Great Western took umbrage. An ultimatum was issued: unless the Great Northern were excluded the Great Western would withdraw all their engines and carriages, and thus leave them with little or no means of working the line. The critical point lay in the locomotives, which according to the Metropolitan Act were required to consume the smoke and condense the exhaust steam.

Myles Fenton, the General Manager of the Metropolitan was not the man to lie down to threats. He sought the help of the Great Northern, and the London and North Western. Both companies offered to loan carriages, and the Great

Northern had a few engines ready for the service that was to begin on September 1st that year. But those few were not nearly enough to handle the full Metropolitan service, and so with only nine days at his disposal, Archibald Sturrock promised to have enough engines adapted in time to work the full service. All other work was stopped at Doncaster. As in building the broad gauge "colossal locomotive" at Swindon in 1846, the shops worked night and day; while in London, in secrecy, and at dead of night the Great Northern engines adapted to condense their own steam, were tried in the Metropolitan tunnels. These "hush-hush" tactics were most successful. Apparently Paddington had no idea of what was going on, and as the days went by the authorities were expecting the Metropolitan surrender hourly. But it never came, and on the night of September 9th, after the last broad gauge train had steamed westwards through the tunnels, Sturrock's engines followed, drawing train after train of narrow gauge stock. It is true that the condensing pipes frequently burst; and one of the Great Northern engines blew its dome off while standing in Bishops Road station. But the day was won, by the man who had once been a tower of strength at Swindon.

Even retracing our steps back to the early "fifties" we are passing out of the pioneer stage of locomotive engineering, yet two more features of operation have to be described. In the earliest days of railways coke was the only locomotive fuel. It was favoured because it was practically smokeless; but it was expensive by comparison with coal, and a great deal of heat was wasted through the flues. Black smoke from an engine chimney is a sign of unburnt fuel, and one of the difficulties with the older forms of fire-box was to secure complete combustion. Robert Stephenson tried to utilise the waste heat in the flues by lengthening the boiler barrel, while a later device was to insert partitions, or "mid-feathers" as they were called, in the fire-box. The solution was obtained in a series of experiments on the Midland Railway between 1856 and 1860. To secure complete combustion of coal an ample supply of air is necessary. With the older types of boiler, the combined effect of the speed of the engine and the fierceness of the blast drew the air entering through the dampers straight through the fire-bed and away to the flues—too quickly for it to be utilised; but building an arch of fire-brick over the grate, so that air coming through the dampers had to turn backwards so to speak, and circumvent the rear end of the arch before going to the flues meant that the air was sweeping horizontally over the fire-bed. In addition to this the secondary air entering through the fire-door was deflected downwards on to the fire. The combined effect of the arch and the deflector plate is, on a well-designed engine, to provide for complete combustion of the fuel, so that even on the heaviest duties a coal burning engine can be run with next to nothing in the way of black smoke. Once the principle of the brick arch was established coal became the standard locomotive fuel in this country.

And so finally we come to John Ramsbottom. This great engineer, perhaps the greatest locomotive man of mid-Victorian times, was responsible for many improvements in locomotive practice. He invented the cast-iron spring packing ring for cylinders, a reversing gear operated by a wheel and screw, instead of the large lever hitherto customary, and he adopted for general use on the London and North Western that clever invention, the injector, for keeping the boiler replenished with water. Then, when one of his draughtsmen suggested the idea of water troughs for taking up water without stopping, he immediately gave instructions for experiments to be made with a view to perfecting the device, so that long runs might be made with the more important express trains. But while Ramsbottom was an excellent practical engineer himself, it was in administration that he so excelled. He was one of the first to appreciate how the cost of locomotive construction and repair could be reduced by standardisation, and having designed an excellent mixed traffic engine, the *DX* 0–6–0, he built no fewer than 943 to the same drawings. Traffic on the L. & N.W.R. was increasing very much, and during his time as chief mechanical engineer the entire scale of the organisation at Crewe had to be greatly expanded. Ramsbottom, indeed, was a major link between the earliest days, and railways almost to the extent that we know them today. He saw the opening of the Liverpool and Manchester Railway, and he himself organised

Crewe to the point of being able to build 100 new locomotives in one year. Again, though he retired in 1871, he lived to a grand old age, till 1897—long enough to learn of the incredible run on the last night of the Anglo-Scottish "race" of 1895, when the 8 p.m. from Euston covered the 540 miles to Aberdeen in 512 minutes.

Of his responsibilities Sir Cusack Roney wrote vividly in 1868:

> At the head of the mighty establishments at Crewe—establishments in which, including men and materials, there is a weekly expenditure of about £20,000—over a million a year—is one who, if he had been in Egypt, with works not a quarter the size and not half so ably carried out, would have been at least a Bey, more probably a Pasha, in Austria a Count of the Holy Empire; in any other country in the world, except in England, with crosses and decorations, the ribbons of which would easily make a charming bonnet of existing dimensions. But in England, the earnest, persevering, never-tiring JOHN RAMSBOTTOM is John Ramsbottom—no more. It is true that he has European and Transatlantic reputation, and that he is Fellow and Honorary Fellow of innumerable societies, thus abnegating in his person the aphorism that says: "Worth makes the man, the want of it the Fellow." For without the worth he would never have been the fellow. Probably had Mr. Ramsbottom been a Member of Parliament he might have had hereditary honours by this time . . .

A charming personality, and a generous contributor to the proceedings of engineering societies, he never sought the limelight of publicity, and retired from active work on the L. & N.W.R. at the early age of fifty-seven. Great though his responsibilities had been, however, they had not included the devastating experiences suffered by the great civil engineers at the time of the Mania, and Ramsbottom retired a fit man. He was to enjoy another twenty-six years of more leisured participation in locomotive work as a director of the Lancashire and Yorkshire Railway, and of Beyer, Peacock and Company.

CHAPTER IV

Some Great Constructional Works

A T the time of the Railway Mania the services of Robert Stephenson, as consultant, were in almost overwhelming demand (10). He took some offices in Great George Street, less than five minutes walk from the Houses of Parliament, and from there he dealt as best he could with an incredible pressure of business. The other leading engineers of the day were in like circumstance. In this year of grace 1954, in which I am writing, engineers in some branches of the profession are inclined to regard themselves as hustling like nothing previously known. Certainly the pace is pretty hot at times; but for the majority, even among senior executives, our lot is placid compared with the lives of Brunel, Locke, Stephenson, and their assistants at the time of the Railway Mania. It was not only the proximity of Parliament that caused the centre of interest in railways to move from the industrial regions to London. In the early days the great business houses of the City hung back in scepticism, waiting to see how the various local railway projects would fare; but when trunk lines such as the London and Birmingham and the Great Western were completed, and obviously proving successful, restraint vanished, and there was a great rush to invest in railways. Shares became a leading feature of business on the Stock Exchange, and the prices of some rose to more than double their original value. This was the signal for an extraordinary period of wild speculation, folly and knavery, and in the general rush to "get rich quick", the true engineers, as distinct from the upstarts who claimed that title, had a gruelling time.

It is to the lasting honour of the railway pioneers that through this fantastic period they kept their heads and their integrity, when by giving countenance to the hordes of schemes on which they were consulted they might have amassed fabulous riches, without any of the ruinous prospects that faced the dupes who were persuaded to invest their money by the sharpers of society. George Stephenson himself must have been a tower of strength to the younger men at this time. The administrative side of railway construction had never been his strong point, as the unfortunate affair of the Grand Junction had shown; but in him cool-headedness and breadth of vision made up for any lack of skill in dealing with "paper-work", and although no man had done more than he towards the inception of the railway network the situation, as it developed in 1845, was so utterly unreal to his practical mind that he stood almost completely aloof. Nevertheless he was often at his son's offices in Great George Street, dressed in black, his tall, spare figure accentuating the rather old-fashioned cut of his tail coat, and a large bunch of seals suspended from his watch ribbon. But above all it was his calm face, clear complexion, and appearance of health and good humour that made him so outstanding a figure among the eager, the harassed, the sordid, and the foolish who milled around on the fringes of this railway maelstrom.

Robert Stephenson was kept almost entirely in London at the time. I have told in the previous chapter how the great invention of the link-motion was conveyed to him from the Forth Street works, in Newcastle, and one feels that if he had had more time to get out on to the railways the shortcomings of the long-boilered express engines might have been more quickly eradicated. As it was, much of his work at that time was hard office slogging of the dullest nature. Samuel Smiles who came to know him well in after years has written:

> During the sittings of the Committees of Parliament, almost every moment of his time was occupied in consultations, and in preparing evidence, or in giving it. The crowded, low-roofed committee rooms of the old Houses of Parliament were altogether inadequate to accommodate the rush of perspiring projectors of bills, and even the lobbies were sometimes choked with them. To have borne that noisome atmosphere and heat would have tested the constitution of salamanders, and engineers

were only human. With brains kept in a state of excitement during the entire day, no wonder their nervous systems became unstrung. Their only chance of refreshment was during an occasional rush to the bun and sandwich stand in the lobby, though sometimes even that resource failed them. Then with mind and body jaded—probably after undergoing a series of consultations upon many bills after the rising of the committees —the exhausted engineers would seek to stimulate nature by a late, perhaps a heavy, dinner. What chance had any ordinary constitution of surviving such an ordeal? The consequence was, that stomach, brain, the liver were alike irretrievably injured; and hence the men who bore the brunt of those struggles— Stephenson, Brunel, Locke and Errington—have already died, comparatively young men.

At the time of the Mania, however, Robert Stephenson's greatest works were still ahead of him, while his father had virtually retired from professional work. He continued to take a great interest in all the genuine work that was going on, though on visiting his son's offices in Westminster, he not infrequently found himself at something of a "loose end". One project in which he naturally showed special concern was the Newcastle and Berwick Railway, which would run past Killingworth and the scenes of his youth. I have told how Brunel did his level best to introduce the "Atmospheric" system for this line, and the success of the Great Western made Brunel a man who was taken very seriously, even in such a stronghold of the Stephenson's as Newcastle. In any case Brunel's advocacy was enough to have Lord Howick, one of the principle promoters, wavering, and he came to Great George Street to talk it over with Robert Stephenson. In the outer office was George Stephenson warming his back at the fire, and guessing the nature of Lord Howick's call he took charge of the situation himself, and told his visitor in no uncertain terms all about "the atmospheric gimcrack", as he always called it. In vain Lord Howick explained that he had come to see Robert Stephenson. Persistently he was bombarded with argument after argument against the atmospheric, until finally he rose to go. George Stephenson followed him down the stairs, and on the doorstep saw him away with the words: "You may take my word for it, my Lord, it will never answer."

But George Stephenson did not always have the opportunity of so demolishing an opponent. Robert Stephenson once said:

When my father came about the office he sometimes did not know what to do with himself. So he used to invite Bidder to have a wrestle with him, for old acquaintance sake. And the two wrestled together so often, and had so many "falls"— sometimes I thought they would bring the house down between them—that they broke half the chairs in my outer office. I remember once sending my father in a joiner's bill of about £2-10-0 for mending broken chairs.

It is hard to imagine how the course of railway history might have been changed if Brunel had won the battle for the Newcastle and Berwick Railway, and laid down the "Atmospheric" system in the heart of the Stephenson country. The Parliamentary contest was long and severe, for Brunel had secured some very powerful backing in the north. But in the event Robert Stephenson won the day, and so it fell to him to complete the line of through railway communication between London and Edinburgh. The line between Newcastle and Tweedmouth was not difficult; the broad valley of the Tweed presented a big obstacle, and at the Newcastle end a further great project was in hand at the same time. The Newcastle and Darlington Junction Railway had hitherto stopped short on the south bank of the Tyne, but now, with the new line to the north sanctioned there was every reason for completing the link-up.

It is perhaps a little difficult nowadays to realise what the gorge of the Tyne was like 110 years ago. Certainly it was dark, but not the black industrialised cutting it is today; it was grand and awe-inspiring in a gloomy kind of way, and the story is told of the Duke of Cumberland on his way to rout the Highland clans at Culloden, shrinking from the prospect of descending to its depths at nightfall in order to cross into Northumberland. The old houses of Newcastle and Gateshead were built on the steep slopes, and the road made a difficult and dangerous descent to the inadequate bridge that crossed the river at the foot of the ravine. The Newcastle Corporation had for many years been aware of the need for improvement; but after the fashion of such bodies the discussions had dragged on for nearly thirty years, and still nothing had been done. The coming of railways changed everything. The idea of a bridge over the Tyne was revived, and the civic authorities "cashed in" on this situation, and insisted that the proposed bridge should carry both rail and road traffic! The High Level Bridge Company was formed in 1843; this was backed by the Newcastle and Darlington Junction Railway, and the Act for construction of the bridge was obtained in 1845.

Across the Tyne the railway tracks were to be carried at the level of the high ground on either side, and on the north bank passing immediately beside the 800-year-old Norman keep of the castle. The conception of the bridge is ingenious, yet very simple. Having in mind the dual purpose of carrying railway and road, Robert Stephenson divided the main portion of the bridge, as distinct from the approaches, into six spans. Each span consisted of a cast-iron arch on top of which the railway was carried, while the roadway is below, suspended from the arch by a series of wrought-iron tie bars. The arches were to be supported on stone piers, and the rails were to be carried at a height of some 130 feet above the river. But the most brilliant conception could be of no avail if suitable foundations were not secured, and in the deep mud and quicksand of the Tyne gorge some very great difficulties were experienced.

The plan of campaign was to build coffer-dams—temporary exclosures extending down to the bed of the river from which the water could be pumped out, and the foundations of the bridge laid in; but the foundation of the coffer-dams was a series of piles to be driven down deep into the firm ground below the river bed. The surveys had indicated that the piles would have to be very massive and long, and Stephenson called to his aid the Nasmyth steam hammer. A temporary viaduct in timber was erected alongside to carry the steam engine and the hammer apparatus. A set of beautiful workings showing details of the temporary bridge, and of stage work in erection of the main viaduct, is preserved in the library of the Institution of Civil Engineers (40). The steam hammer worked magnificently. It was

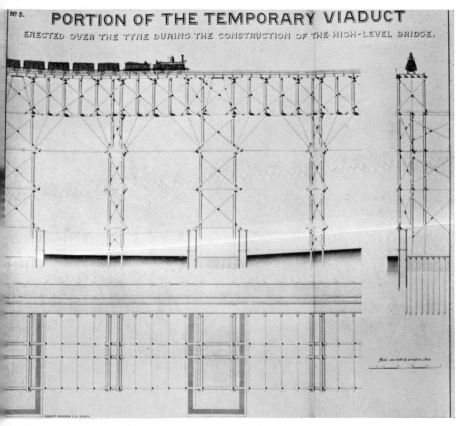

PORTION OF THE TEMPORARY VIADUCT
ERECTED OVER THE TYNE DURING THE CONSTRUCTION OF THE HIGH-LEVEL BRIDGE.

40   Portion of the temporary viaduct erected over the River Tyne during
construction of the High Level Bridge (*Robert Stephenson, engineer*)

From a series of drawings in the possession of the Institution of Civil Engineers

41　A Sinclair express locomotive, Great Eastern Railway, as later rebuilt

42　Bury 0–4–0 with haystack firebox ("Coppernobs"), Furness Railway

the first application of this form of power to bridge pile-driving. Two hammers of 1½ tons each were kept in regular use, each making between sixty and seventy strokes per minute; many times the pile-head burst into flames during the process of driving, and as soon as one pile was driven the next one was presented. One must be pardoned, however, for treating Samuel Smiles description as a picturesque exaggeration: "down it went", he wrote, "into the solid bed of the river, with almost as much ease as a lady sticks pins into a cushion!"

Difficulties were not at an end with the driving of the piles and the building of the coffer-dams. In one case there was quicksand below. This must have given Robert Stephenson some ugly memories of Kilsby Tunnel, though in the Tyne Gorge no serious accident occurred. It was just that they could not clear the inside of the coffer-dam of water; it came in from below as fast as it was pumped out. Pumping went on for months; increasing the capacity of the pumps had absolutely no effect, until at last almost as a measure of desperation the expedient was tried of sealing the inrush with cement. Once this was set the bottom, to everyone's relief, was found to be secure, and with the inside of the coffer-dam dry at last a concrete bed was built up to the level of the piling. The foundation course of stone blocks was laid about two feet below low-water mark. In connection with the sealing of the quicksand with concrete it is of interest that a fissure in the rocks above the Severn Tunnel which was causing serious leakage of water into the tunnel itself in 1929, was counteracted in the same way, by sealing the area of the fissure in the river bed by dumping bags of cement. The High Level Bridge at Newcastle was a massively constructed, yet very graceful bridge. It has stood the test of time, and today carries a very heavy traffic. The main structure has remained in perfect condition, and the only parts that have ever needed attention and renewal over a period of a hundred years are the connections to the subsidiary members carrying the rails.

The completion of the bridge in 1849 was a great day for Newcastle and Gateshead. On June 7th the last key of the rails was driven home by the Mayor of Gateshead; on

9

August 15th the first passenger train crossed the Tyne, and
the rejoicings were consummated on September 28th, when
Queen Victoria crossed in the Royal Train on her way southwards from Balmoral, and the bridge was officially declared
open. Royal visits to the provincial cities were few and far
between at that period in our history. The last occasion on
which a reigning sovereign had visited Tyneside had been
in 1646, and then it was hardly a time for rejoicing; Charles I
had, by that late stage in the Civil War, given himself up
to the Scottish army, and he was brought to Newcastle as
a prisoner! But Queen Victoria and the Prince Consort did
not tarry long; she arrived shortly after noon, duly received
addresses of welcome—on the bridge itself—from the Mayors
of Newcastle, and Gateshead, and *in fifteen minutes* resumed
her journey south. Robert Stephenson was offered a knighthood, but he declined the honour. On the same day the
Queen had passed for the first time over the Royal Border
Bridge crossing the Tweed at Berwick, and the train had
been halted for a few minutes to enable her to enjoy the
magnificent view from that lofty parade ground. Smiles
records that a triumphal arch was erected over the tracks at
Berwick station, on which were blazoned the words: "The
Last Act of the Union".

It was in no burst of sentimentalism that Stephenson's
famous biographer recalled the stormy history of Berwick,
and that the district in which the bridge stands had been
the scene of constant warfare. Long after declared warfare
between Scots and English had ceased, the border country
was a wild, debatable "no-mans land", and no more than
a hundred years earlier than the commencement of work on
Stephenson's bridge, the Highland Clans under the leadership of Bonnie Prince Charlie, had invaded England. As if
to signalise the ending of the bad old days the railway from
the south cut clean through the castle battlements at
Berwick. Nevertheless on the many occasions on which I
have ridden north on the engines of Anglo-Scottish expresses,
I have never yet failed to experience a tremendous thrill as
we come out on to the cliff above Spittal, see the town of
Berwick with its red-roofed houses, its church spires, and its
battlements still looking every inch the frontier fortress.

And then as we sweep down through Tweedmouth and round the curve towards the Royal Border Bridge, can one be surprised that thoughts of Robert Stephenson and his works come flashing through the mind. Nowadays the crack expresses do not even stop at Berwick; in the summer months the *Elizabethan* does not stop anywhere between London and Edinburgh. But they all pass over Stephenson's bridge, which apart from ordinary maintenance work is just as he completed it 105 years ago.

From the Stephenson's and their triumphs we turn for a moment to the unlucky Vignoles (62), and his brief association with the railway originally known as the Sheffield, Ashton-under-Lyne, and Manchester. Although taking us a little backwards in railway history, to the year 1836, this original project has a particular interest today in that the line has recently been converted to electric traction to cope with the enormous mineral traffic that is carried. When the line was first promoted Vignoles was appointed as engineer. Prior to this Locke had also been consulted, and even after the appointment of Vignoles some of the promoters seemed anxious to have a second opinion at every stage. This might have given rise to much unpleasantness; but apparently Vignoles was brimming over with enthusiasm, and generally speaking such associations as he had with Locke in the preliminary days were friendly enough. But while Locke was always cautiousness itself, especially where estimates and money were concerned, Vignoles was apt to be carried away by his enthusiasm. About the same time he was associated with John Braithwaite in conducting the bill for the Eastern Counties Railway through Parliament, and obstruction arose from the want of willingness on the part of the solicitors to advance the necessary funds. Vignoles, without any hesitation offered to make himself responsible!

With the Sheffield and Manchester line commencement of the work was at first delayed by lack of funds. Vignoles, characteristically, had already taken a number of shares himself; he induced some of his relatives to do the same, and it might well have seemed strange for the engineer to canvas many business houses in the City of London with a view to their becoming shareholders. Yet so Vignoles did, and when

9*

some of the Manchester subscribers began to grow apprehensive of success and gave up their holdings Vignoles went to the stage of buying up large quantities of the depreciated shares. It seemed as though his whole existence was wrapt up in this railway. Unlike other speculators of the Mania period his motives appear to have been solely the furtherance of the company's well-being. In 1838 he was duly selected as engineer-in-chief for the construction of the line, and with his usual zeal he threw his whole strength into the job. A large staff and labour force was engaged, and operations were commenced at the Manchester end. In profile the line can be likened to a huge gable, having its apex at the point where the railway was carried in a tunnel under the Pennines. And what a tunnel! At that time only two major tunnels had been driven in the construction of railways in England; of these the notorious Kilsby was 2,425 yards long, while Box, on the Great Western was 3,230 yards. Yet out in the wilderness of Woodhead Moor the Sheffield Railway was to pass through a tunnel 5,300 yards long, blasted from the millstone grit of the Pennines.

Vignoles seems to have realised that here was his great opportunity, by carrying through this tremendous work to put himself alongside the greatest engineers of the day. To his zeal was added immense confidence in himself, which, however, a small minority of the directors did not share. It was from this quarter that the earlier insistence upon a second opinion had come. Vignoles had something of the Brunellian touch about him, in the way everything he did had to be done in handsome style—one might almost say regardless of cost. He took a beautiful country house at Dinting Vale, and brought his younger children there from London; a resident tutor was engaged, and with all at first going well on the railway it seemed at last that his star was really in the ascendant. Work had begun on the Woodhead Tunnel, though here his estimates seem to have omitted to include any accommodation for the workmen. Even today there are many stretches where there is no human habitation in sight, and when Vignoles got to work in 1838 the entire countryside was depopulated. Then, when the problem presented itself, he urged the directors to provide tents for the workmen. Difficulties were arising in other ways. Some of his opponents on the board took quite uncalled-for liberties when visiting the tunnel works, giving instructions to individual employees, and even countermanding the orders Vignoles had previously issued. There seems little doubt that such tactics were used deliberately, knowing that with his fiery temperament he would rise to the bait. He did, and there were many cases of strained loyalties. Nevertheless, Vignoles's enthusiasm still carried him along, and when his eldest son came of age, in August 1839, the event was signalised by great festivities at his home at Dinting Vale. The entertainment was on the most lavish scale; all the gentry for miles around were invited, and with them, of course, the directors of the company and the principal officers. A month later the shadows began to close in upon Vignoles.

It was about this time that he began to feel the financial strain of the 1,402 shares he held in the company, with a liability upon them of £140,000. Accordingly, after taking advice of two of his firmest friends among the Sheffield section of the board, he went with them to see Lord Wharncliffe, the Chairman, and to explain the circumstances. He asked to be relieved of at least some of the liability. The matter was referred to a meeting of shareholders in October 1839, at which meeting Lord Wharncliffe said in respect of Vignoles's holdings: "This gentleman, in August 1837, being very anxious that the threatened break-up of the company should be avoided, thought fit to buy up this vast number of shares and distribute them to his various friends in small apportionments, under a guarantee that they should not be called upon to pay up. . . ."

A committee of directors appointed to deal with the matter met Vignoles next day, and after a long conference a compromise was agreed upon, that the engineer should forfeit all the shares he had brought, and thus lose the money he had paid for them in the first place. But beyond that, Lord Wharncliffe promised, no further claim would be made upon him or his friends who held shares. This was a blow sufficiently heavy, involving a loss of some £10,000, but, of course, it also compelled his resignation from the post of engineer. But, he thought, it put his friends in the clear. The worst, however.

was to follow. The Board refused to confirm the arrangements between Lord Wharncliffe and Vignoles; the Manchester section were determined to enforce their rights to the uttermost, and appealed to law. The case went against Vignoles, with the result that not only was he faced with a personal loss of £80,000, but, as he wrote in his diary for January 15th, 1841:

> a great number of my friends will be utterly ruined, and the rest either cruelly embarrassed or obliged to go through the *Gazette*! Considering in what way I could assist some of them to meet the cruel pressure that will immediately be put on them. Half distracted at the frightful prospect before us all!
> Good God! that men whom I had served so faithfully, and for whose railway I had done so much, should act like this!

That Vignoles never flinched under the terrible results of his zeal to help the Manchester and Sheffield line, and continued his professional work with undiminished vigour and skill is a tribute to a great personality. In appraising the present developments on that line, the completion of the third Woodhead Tunnel, and the inauguration of electric traction, one cannot but think back wistfully to the crushing misfortune suffered by the first engineer-in-chief.

Lord Wharncliffe, and most of the Sheffield section of the directors had resigned when their agreement with Vignoles was not ratified; and it was no more than natural that the reconstituted Board should invite Joseph Locke to become engineer-in-chief(18). He found, much as he had done on the Southampton Railway, that his predecessor had let the work in small contracts to small men. Locke's biographer tends to exaggerate the confused situation that had developed in the early stages of the boring of Woodhead Tunnel; but the new engineer managed to secure the services of Nicholas Wood as contractor-in-chief for the tunnel, and against Vignoles estimate of £98,000 Locke told the directors it would cost at least double! Due to lack of funds the tunnel was in any case to be made for a single line of rails only. One could hardly blame the investors of 1837–9 for not having more confidence in the project, and for holding back; but the fact remains that their attitude—faint-heartedness, parsimony, or however it may be regarded—eventually cost The Railway Executive of our own times 4¼ million pounds! Be that as it may, back in 1839 Joseph Locke quickly brought his clear brain and superb organising skill to the great task of boring the first Woodhead Tunnel. His biographer tells us that the job of getting supplies forward was as bad as supporting the Crimean army before Balaklava! The contractors built shops of their own; sometimes the men were paid in food, and they camped in huts, quickly run up with loose stones and mud, and thatched with heather. They slept upon improvised truckle beds, twenty together. It was a tremendous task. The tunnel was driven from two portals and five intermediate shafts, though no technical description of the work has survived. Driving in from the open hillside at the Woodhead portal the rocks are hard gritstone and sandstone at first, but then comes a thick slanting layer of that most treacherous of rock formations—shale. Although there is no direct evidence it would seem certain that serious trouble with rock falls occurred; in any case during the six years it was under construction the first Woodhead Tunnel claimed the high casualty list of 28 killed, 200 seriously injured or disabled, and 450 lesser accidents.

Eventually it took six years to complete, and on December 20th, 1845, it was ready for the Government Inspection, by General Pasley. The execution of the work was first class, though against the naked rock-faces the castellated portals looked rather grim. At the western end the effect was heightened by some grotesque gargoyles over the entrance! General Pasley said that it was one of the finest pieces of engineering he had ever seen, and it was opened for traffic just before Christmas 1845. The short-sightedness of the original decision to have a single tracked bore was apparent before the line had been open two years! And while the engineering work to build a double line tunnel in the first place would not have been greatly more difficult in 1847 the railway embarked upon the costly job of boring a duplicate tunnel alongside the older one, and this took a further five years to complete. The original cost borne by the railway was thus very much greater than would have been the case if a double-line tunnel had been driven in the first place. Moreover, the two single line bores were to bring troubles of their own later. Towards the end of the Second World War deterioration became evident. Maintenance was never easy, due to the volume of traffic and the restricted space available, and eventually the situation grew so serious, that in 1946 the drastic step was taken of giving the engineer absolute possession of each tunnel alternately over a period of nine months, so that repair work could proceed night and day. The consequent delays were so serious, however, and the volume of repair work needed so great, that eventually the London and North Eastern Railway engineers had to give up the task and recommend the building of an entirely new tunnel.

In view of the early history of the original tunnels, it is of particular interest to compare the relative estimates made for the new work in 1947. Three alternatives were considered:

(a) to build one new single line tunnel and repair one of the old ones;
(b) to build two new single tunnels;
(c) to build a new double-line tunnel and abandon the old ones completely.

This last course proved the cheapest of all, according to the 1947 estimates, while the cost of building two new single-line tunnels was estimated at 43 per cent more than that of building one double-line bore. Against Locke's original estimate of 1839, £200,000 for one single-line tunnel, and presumably £400,000 for the twin bores eventually built, the actual cost of the new double-line tunnel completed in 1954 came out to £4,250,000. By this staggering amount has the cost of railway construction increased in a hundred years!

Returning to pioneer days, Joseph Locke was the engineer for another famous mountain line, the Lancaster and Carlisle. Strangely enough this does not include one single tunnel, but the chief topographical feature of the route is the notorious Shap incline where the track is carried over the water-shed between the Lune and the Lowther at an altitude of 915 feet above sea-level. In certain quarters Locke was severely criticised for this route. George Stephenson advocated passing on level track round the Cumberland coast, and putting the coal and iron districts of Whitehaven and Workington on the main line to Scotland. But Locke's route was only 60 miles long, against 90 miles round the coast, and he won the day. Even in these days of giant "Pacific" engines, however, the flowery journalese of a contemporary writer could only be regarded as a picturesque flight of the imagination. "Over Shap Fell", he wrote, "the locomotive speeds with the rapidity of an arrow, arousing the bittern from its solitude, at a height which the eagle once claimed for its eyrie. . . ." There is not much of the arrow-flight about the *Mid-day Scot* or the night *Postal* pounding its way up the long bank, high above the town of Kendal, and one can hardly imagine that Alexander Allan's little engines did much better one hundred years ago! Still the road is a magnificent one, in the prospects it affords of the lone Westmorland Fells, of the Lune Gorge, and of the bleak limitless moorlands of Shap.

There is another side to railway construction. Devey, in his life of Joseph Locke, touches a very human aspect, that of the small property owner whose land is cut up to make the railway. Rich and powerful interests might secure a diversion of a proposed line so as to skirt their lands, but the small man was well-nigh helpless. Wordsworth looked on coldly from his home in the Lake District until Locke came to build the branch line through Kendal to Windermere, and the property of a friend was threatened. He has written of the intense love felt by many of the yeomen for their small inheritances, and how when a neighbour of one such man suggested he should fell a tree, and sell it for profit, exclaimed: "Fell it? I had rather fall on my knees and worship it." When Wordsworth heard that the new railway was to pass through this little property he poured out his heart:

> Is then no nook of English ground secure
> From rash assault? Schemes of retirement sown
> In youth, and 'mid the busy world kept pure
> As when their earliest flowers of hope were blown,
> Must perish; how can they this blight endure?
> And must he too the ruthless change bemoan
> Who scorns a false utilitarian lure
> 'Mid his paternal fields at random thrown?

It would no doubt be of small comfort to the outraged yeoman, or to Wordsworth, to know that Locke was a great lover of poetry, and always carried a copy of Byron in his pocket!

Wordsworth did not rant against the coming of railway as Ruskin. He saw, even before the Mania was working up to its height the danger of a decline in spiritual values. But: ".... the thirst of Gold that rules o'er Britain like a baneful star", was no new thing in 1844 when he wrote the sonnet "Proud were ye, Mountains . . ." It was the building of a line like the Lancaster and Carlisle, bringing evidence of the new age near to his beloved Lakeland country that caused him to weigh so heavily against it. And yet, shrewd observer as he was, he came to see another side to constructional days in surprising and beautiful circumstances. On June 21st, 1845, he wrote the sonnet "At Furness Abbey":

> Well have yon Railway Labourers to THIS ground
> Withdrawn for noonday rest. They sit, they walk
> Among the Ruins, but no idle talk
> Is heard; to grave demeanour all are bound;
> And from one voice a Hymn with tuneful sound
> Hallows once more the long-deserted Quire
> And thrills the old sepulchral earth, around.
> Others look up, and with fixed eyes admire
> That wide spanned arch, wondering how it was raised,
> To keep, so high in air, its strength and grace;
> All seem to feel the spirit of the place,
> And by the general reverence God is praised:
> Profane Despoilers, stand ye not reproved,
> While thus these simple-hearted men are moved?

This charming sonnet hardly suggests the riotous crew portrayed in more popular descriptions of the English railway navvy!

The first Woodhead Tunnel and the Lancaster and Carlisle were among the greatest of Locke's railways in this country, and we must now pass on to another great feat of cutting and tunnelling, the South Eastern Railway, between Folkestone and Dover. The original main line as laid out by William Cubitt set out from a junction with the Brighton line at Redhill; it was carried on a magnificently straight and easy course through the Weald of Kent, till Folkestone was reached. There, an abrupt change in the geological formation was obviously going to involve heavy engineering works, and the prospect of that range of lofty white cliffs, rising at times sheer from the sea, might well cause any engineer to pause and consider alternative ways of reaching Dover. Even before the chalk was entered there was the Foord gap. In crossing the greensand ridge that blocks in the eastern end of the Weald the railway approached Folkestone at high level, and a viaduct of nineteen arches having a maximum height of 100 feet was necessary over the valley looking down to the narrow winding streets of Old Folkestone. Even then, although the white cliffs are near at hand, a ridge of hard gault outcrops the chalk before the undercliff of the Folkestone Warren is reached. The line is carried through the gault in the Martello Tunnel, so named from the watch tower of Napoleonic days on the shore nearby. There was tough work in the making of this tunnel, but the most spectacular engineering is to be seen further on.

The line is carried in cuttings through the wild, tumbled undercliff region of the Warren until the huge mass of Abbots Cliff rises ahead; through this Cubitt drove a long tunnel (43). Although fairly close to the sea the chalk is very sound, and his judgment is this respect has been well proved by the years; the tunnel is as good as ever today, after 110 years. On emerging from the eastern end of Abbots Cliff Tunnel the line had to be carried on a ledge cut in the chalk, above which the cliffs rose to a great height. Right in the way was the Round Down Cliff, 375 feet above high-water mark, the formation of which was at the most favourable estimate treacherous. To tunnel would have been hazardous, and the plan Cubitt conceived was so novel, and likely to be so spectacular that he consulted General Pasley, of the Board of Trade before embarking on it. His plan was nothing less than to blow the cliff out of the way in one gigantic blasting operation! General Pasley agreed, and suggested that the services of Lieutenant Hutchinson, R.E., should be requested, as that officer had had a similar experience of firing three big charges simultaneously in removing the wreck of the *Royal George*. Hutchinson was duly consulted. Three shafts were sunk from the top of the cliff, and from each a gallery was run 300 ft. long. Into the foot of each shaft the explosive charges were packed; a 5,500 lb. charge in each of the outer shafts, and 7,500 lb. in the central one.

The operation was carried out on January 26th, 1843, and a vivid description was published in *The Times*:

> At exactly 26 minutes past 2 o'clock a low, faint, indistinct, indescribable moaning rumble was heard and immediately afterwards the bottom of the cliff began to belly out, and then almost simultaneously about 500 ft. in breadth of the summit began gradually, but rapidly to sink. There was no roaring explosion, no bursting out of fire, no violent and crushing splitting of rocks and comparatively speaking very little smoke, for a proceeding of mighty and irresponsible force it had little or nothing of the appearance of force.

After the debris had been cleared, the embankment on which the railway was to be carried at the base of the cliffs, was protected by a massive concrete sea wall. There was, however, still one more obstruction to be cleared before Dover was attained, the famous bluff known as Shakespeare's Cliff. Cubitt does not seem to have been quite so sure of the chalk here as he was at Abbots Cliff, for whereas in the latter tunnel he used a normal double-line bore at Shakespeare's Cliff he went to the expense of two separate tunnels at some little distance apart, and built them in the shape of a very tall Gothic arch. From Shakespeare's Cliff Tunnel a timber viaduct across the beach completed the remarkable eight miles of railway that began at the western end of the Foord viaduct.

It was no more than natural that some apprehension was felt for the continuing safety of such a line. Even before it was opened, the critics were saying that trains would be overwhelmed by falls in the chalk, or that the embankments would be undermined by the sea. General Pasley carried out the Government inspection, and found not the slightest cause for apprehension. He went meticulously over the ground above the tunnels, and above the open stretch where the Round Down Cliff had once stood, but could find no unsound parts as would be revealed by cracks above. In his report he stresses the point that the tunnels were made in the

44 Conway Tubular Bridge under construction
Robert Stephenson, engineer

43 Abbots Cliff Tunnel: western end
(South Eastern Railway)
William Cubitt, engineer

45 Shakespeare's Cliff Tunnel and Viaduct, South Eastern Railway

William Cubitt, engineer

soundest part of the chalk, with a considerable height of
solid chalk between them and the sea, and also above it.
The viaduct over the beach was carried on piles driven down
into the solid chalk. The tunnels and the sea wall between
them stand four-square today. The viaduct remained until
1927, and was removed then on account of railway extensions
which required more than two lines of rails. Where trouble
has occurred on the Folkestone–Dover section has been in the
Warren. There was a bad landslip in December 1915 that
completely blocked the line, and similar, though not-so-
extensive troubles have occurred since. These have been due
to erosion of the chalk by the sea, and at the present time
elaborate coast defence works have been installed at the most
prevalent danger spot just to the east of Martello Tunnel.

Sir William Cubitt, as he afterwards became, was never a
railway engineer in the sense that one regards the Stephensons, Brunel, and Locke. The other line in connection with
which he will be remembered was the Great Northern, and
this line, like the South Eastern was laid out for fast running.
It was remarkable that the stretch through the chalk
between Folkestone and Dover originally had no change of
gradient worth mentioning, though there are now certain
variations due to the landslips in the Warren, and other
incidental causes. Cubitt's association with the Great
Northern is perhaps best remembered by the dramatic manner of his appointment. The "London and York", as it was
originally known was bitterly opposed by those interests,
centred upon Derby, who sought to keep the whole traffic
from London to the north-eastern counties to the Midland
group of lines. This short-sighted view was in some contrast
to George Stephenson's vision of a railway network over the
whole country; but the London and York had in Edmund
Denison a Chairman who was not to be stopped, and the
line was authorised in 1844. At the outset Locke was
appointed as engineer-in-chief. He was then busy with the
Rouen Railway, and evidently felt that he had enough on
hand, for very soon after he resigned. After all the criticism
and scorn that had been poured upon the project by its
opponnets in the Parliamentary stage it had been a triumph
to secure the services of an engineer whose reputation stood

10

second only to that of Robert Stephenson; but then his
sudden resignation, understandable though it might have
been from his own point of view, might have been a tragedy
for the London and York, through loss of prestige.

Denison as usual acted like lightning. In his view there
was only one alternative for the post, William Cubitt, who
had come very much into the public eye from his spectacular
work between Dover and Folkestone in the previous year.
The letter bringing Locke's resignation reached Denison on
a Friday night. Late though it was he ordered his carriage
at once and drove out to Cubitt's house on Clapham Common.
All was in darkness, but Denison was not to be deterred, and
he hammered repeatedly on the door. Suddenly a first-floor
window was flung open and Cubitt himself, furious and
bedecked in night-cap demanded to know what all the noise
was about.

"Will you be the engineer of the London and York,"
shouted Denison from below.

"Eh, what has happened to Locke?"

"Resigned. Will you take his place?"

"Yes. I'll come and see you in the morning."

And that was that! The newspapers of Monday, September
23rd, announced Locke's resignation and Cubitt's appointment simultaneously.

From an early date in railway history, attention was
focused on the need for establishing better communication
with Ireland. In the year 1836 an Irish Railway Commission
had been set up, and a major project before them was that
of the route to be taken from London by the Irish Mail.
Since the construction of Telford's great highway, and the
completion of the Menai suspension bridge in 1826 (46), the
mail packets had sailed from Holyhead, but with the coming
of railways it was vastly quicker to use Liverpool; although
the sea voyage was much longer, it was found possible to
bring the journey time from London to Dublin down from
a little over two days to $22\frac{1}{2}$ hours. But Liverpool was
obviously not the best place for an Irish packet station, and
at one time Port Dinlleyn was strongly favoured. Here was
a small, though good natural harbour half-way up the

western coast of the Lleyn peninsular; it was favoured by certain influential men of the Admiralty, and both Cubitt and Vignoles reported in favour in evidence they gave before the Irish Railway Commissioners. For some time now Port Dinlleyn has been known as Nevin. It was particularly attractive to Vignoles, for it fitted in well as a terminus of a route across Wales that he strongly advocated. But other interests were also at work. George Stephenson made a survey from Chester to Holyhead, following the coast for most of the way. Special commissions were set up to examine the merits of both routes and packet stations. Local interests in Chester were anxious to see their city on the main line of communication between London and Dublin, and they invited George Stephenson to report on the relative merits of the two routes proposed. It was hardly to be expected that he would do otherwise than commend the route he himself had surveyed, and he went so far as to suggest that the rival route through the mountains was almost impracticable.

Although a special committee of the House of Commons had reported strongly in favour of the Chester and Holyhead route events dragged on with no immediate action, and in the summer of 1843 Brunel asked Vignoles to make a more detailed survey of the route to Port Dinlleyn. This was to follow the existing route via Oxford as far as Worcester, then to run via Ludlow, Craven Arms, Montgomery, and Newtown. So far was relatively easy ground, but then came the Carno Pass through which the line to Aberystwyth now runs. Turning rightwards from the lower reaches of the pass Vignoles proposed to tunnel under the flanks of Cader Idris, to pass Dolgelly, and reach the Irish packet station by a route round the shores of Tremadoc Bay. Had this route ever been constructed as a main line in the Brunellian style, the coastal towns of Barmouth, Portmadoc, Criccieth and Pwllheli might by this time have formed, between them, a serious rival to Torbay! But the choice went in favour of Holyhead, and the proposed trunk line to Pwllheli was never made. Today a rather charming "back of beyond" atmosphere prevails around the head of Tremadoc Bay, and the Cambrian Coast Express, despite its high-sounding name, take all but eight hours to cover the 270 miles from Paddington.

The Chester and Holyhead Railway Act received the Royal Assent on July 4th, 1844; Robert Stephenson was appointed engineer, and although for the major part of its length the route was an easy one, the crossing of the Conway river and of the Menai Strait, together with the negotiating of Penmaenmawr headland provided him with opportunities for building some of the greatest works of his whole career. There could scarcely have been a greater contrast between the Parliamentary proceedings over this railway, and those of the Liverpool and Manchester. The Chester and Holyhead, with Government backing went through almost without comment, let alone opposition; and whereas every detail of the earlier line had been fought over, the Chester and Holyhead bill went through before the design of the two great bridges had been properly formulated, still less finished. The crossing of the Menai Strait was by far the greater of the two tasks. At a point about two miles south-west of Bangor, where the Strait is almost at its narrowest the Britannia Rock lay in mid-stream. While this seemed an obvious point to erect the bridge the width from shore to shore is about 1,100 ft. Stephenson's first proposal was to use two main spans of 350 ft. each, springing from the central rock, each arch to be built up from cast-iron members. Similar proposals had previously been put forward by John Rennie, and again by Telford, for carrying the Holyhead road, and both had been rejected by the Admiralty. At this length of time it is difficult to appreciate why the navigation of the Strait was considered of such vital importance, when vessels could, with little extra time and trouble have sailed round the coast of Anglesey; but the fact remains that the Admiralty had the right of veto, and any bridge that required scaffolding or support from beneath during construction was not permitted. It was certainly a tremendous problem, for which no previous experience existed; for without scaffolding each span of the bridge would have to be made complete, and then, somehow, manœuvred into position.

At that stage in engineering history knowledge of the behaviour of wrought-iron was elementary, but as rough calculations were made it was evident that with spans of the gigantic size needed at the Menai Strait almost the entire

46 Panoramic view of the Menai Strait, showing Telford's Suspension Bridge, and the
Tubular Bridge in the distance

From a lithograph after T. Picken

47   The huge sculptured lions for the Britannia Bridge entrance

48   Building of Conway Tubular Bridge: men at capstan hauling a floating tube into place

From a drawing by G. Hawkins

49   Construction of one of the tubes

50   A general view of the works
From contemporary engravings

BUILDING THE BRITANNIA BRIDGE

problem would be to make the spans strong enough to support themselves; the additional weight of trains, if not negligible, would be a minor consideration. Stephenson's first essay towards the bridge took the form of a box girder, strongly braced in all directions, and supported by chains from the towers to give increased security—a kind of suspension bridge, but with the platform rigid instead of flexible. This proposal was afterwards modified to have first circular, and then elliptical tubes, instead of rectangular ones, and in March 1845 he gave instructions for drawings to be prepared. In due course some models were made and tested; but they failed, and in the face of this disappointment gradually there emerged the idea of a rectangular tube for each line of railway with the trains running through it. A further model was made, and tested by adding weights. By adding more and more weights to the model Stephenson sought, by the most practical means, to discover the weakest part of his structure, and this model failed by the buckling of the plates in the top edge, or boom. It is a striking commentary upon the imperfect knowledge of engineering materials existing at that time that until this test it was not known that wrought-iron was weakest in compression—in contrast to the better-known property of cast-iron, weakest in tension. The booms of the rectangular tubes had to be strengthened.

But time was pressing on, and the directors of the Chester and Holyhead Railway were growing impatient. It seemed as though the bridges at Conway and the Menai Strait would not be ready in time for the projected opening of the line. Stephenson, however, proceeded with the utmost caution. It was the year of the Mania, and his whole existence was one of intense interviews, Parliamentary committees, and feverish work in London, quite apart from the tremendous responsibility of the Menai bridge. He was fortunate at this stage in having an able and devoted assistant in Edwin Clark, and having the co-operation of William Fairbairn, the great shipbuilder of Millwall. While Clark prepared the ground for experiment, Fairbairn built the models. The final test was indeed a mighty experiment in itself. A model one-sixth full size was built, and since the longest of the Britannia tubes was to be 450 ft. the model was no less than 75 ft. long; it was 4 ft. 6 in. deep, 2 ft. 8 in. high, and weighed between 5 and 6 tons. It was then mounted on supports, and loading commenced. When carrying a weight of 30 tons it broke across the bottom boom; strengthening was added, further fractures occurred, and still more iron was put on. Eventually the great tube was at last equally strong all over, and supported the astonishing weight of 86 tons. Since the experiments began fully one ton of extra iron had been built into the structure, but by the process of trial and error it had, in due course, been built into the right place. The experiments continued until April 1847 before Stephenson was finally satisfied—satisfied, moreover, that the tube was of sufficient strength to support itself without the aid of auxiliary chains. The idea of using chains was widely known at the time, and, indeed, some artists duly included in their drawings of the bridge these non-existent accessories!

The next problem was to erect the tubes and raise them to their ultimate resting places on the towers. Huge platforms and workshops were built alongside the waterways, both at Conway and in the Straits (44); the iron plates were brought in shiploads from Liverpool; cottages were erected for the workmen, and for a time these quiet shores were transformed into the likeness of shipyards, with the clanging of hammers, the noise of riveting, mingled with the periodic explosions as the rocks were blasted away to form the foundations. At the height of the activity nearly 1,500 men were engaged on the Britannia bridge alone (50). As finally designed the two central spans of the bridge were 460 ft. long, and each tube weighed about 1,350 tons. The plan of erection was to build them on pontoons at the shore, float them into position at high tide, manœuvre them on to supports in the towers where they would be left hanging when the tide fell. Then they were to be raised, little by little, by jacks, and the masonry built in beneath. The conception was brilliant in its simplicity, but tubes of 1,350 tons weight floating on the strong tides that run in the Menai Straits might easily prove unmanageable.

There is no doubt that the strain of preparation told heavily on Stephenson. Years after, he told Gooch: "It was

a most anxious and harassing time with me. Often at night
I would lie tossing about, seeking sleep in vain. The tubes
filled my head. I went to bed with them and got up with
them. In the grey of the morning, when I looked across the
Square, it seemed an immense distance across to the houses
on the opposite side. It was nearly the same length as the
span of my tubular bridge!" In addition to his own assistants, and his partner G. P. Bidder, his friends Locke and
Brunel gave freely of their time and experience, while for
the critical operation of floating the tubes he enlisted the aid
of Captain Claxton of the Royal Navy (48). The Conway
bridge was tackled first; it was slightly shorter than the
longest of the Menai spans, and at high tide the water was
not subject to the strong currents experienced in the Straits.
Nevertheless it was a novel and hazardous undertaking, in
which team work between the various gangs of men working
the tow lines was all-important. On March 6th, 1848, the
first Conway tube was floated. Stephenson directed the
whole operation in person; Locke and Brunel were also there,
while Captain Claxton was in charge of the amphibious
operations. It is, I think, one of the happiest episodes in all
British railway engineering history that two men who were
at the very top of their profession, and who were often in
open rivalry to him should have come to Stephenson as
"volunteer assistants" in these outstanding works. In later
years, too, Brunel sought the help of Robert Stephenson,
and received it in full measure.

The first tube was floated successfully at Conway, and
this operation provided a most useful rehearsal for the more
difficult job at the Menai Straits. At Conway the height
above the water was quite small, and the first tube was in
its final resting-place by April 16th, 1848. Two days later
Robert Stephenson drove the first locomotive through the
tube. Work then proceeded with the second of the Conway
tubes, while in the light of experience gained in floating the
pontoons preparations were made for the great operations
at the Menai Straits. Stephenson's anxieties were certainly
not lessened, and then in August 1848 his beloved father
died in his home at Tapton House. In private and public
utterances afterwards, Robert Stephenson never lost one

opportunity for paying tribute to the memory of his father, and it was a matter of great sorrow to him that George Stephenson did not live to see the Britannia Bridge completed. When the time came for floating the first tube great excitement prevailed. Thousands of spectators gathered along the Carnarvon shore, but on June 19th, 1849, the day originally fixed for the operation the weather was unfavourable, and Stephenson postponed it. Great was the surprise and merriment next morning when it was found that one of the daily newspapers contained a vivid account of how the tube had been floated into position! On this following day, however, June 20th, the operation was carried through, and as the tube was at last brought safely to its anchorage on the towers, after several exciting though minor mishaps, the crowd, which had been intensely quiet during the whole floating, burst forth into cheers of enthusiasm mingled with relief.

By this time Stephenson was showing the strain, and when a friend said to him: "This great work has made you ten years older", he replied, "I have not slept sound for three weeks." But from this stage the building of the bridge went on rapidly, and in less than a year Stephenson himself drove the last rivet. As to the appearance of the bridge, with its great towers, and those colossal sculptured lions guarding the entrance, a contemporary account written by the Rev. W. E. Dickson in 1854 gives an unusually vivid description, at a time when accounts of such works were apt to be grotesque in their strivings for effect. Dickson, saying that the onlooker will be amazed at the prodigious massiveness of the masonry, and the beautiful symmetry of the ironwork, goes on:

The tubes, as seen in long perspective, present an endless series of rivets, following, in accurately straight lines, the edges of the plates: while the immense towers convey to the mind an irresistible impression of unshakeable stability and eternal duration.

The writer visited this magnificent bridge on the 18th June 1851, during the occurrence of a solar eclipse: and he is unable to record in fitting terms, the sensations of astonishment, admiration, and even awe, which the sight awakened in his mind. Seen under the varying effects of light and shade produced by the eclipse, the Tubular Bridge appeared to him to harmonize wonderfully with the scene around: and though he was conscious that he gazed on a work designed and executed by man, he could not but feel that the praise and glory should be ascribed, not to man, but to Him by whom man's mind was given, and man's energies sustained. That majestic structure was but an illustration of the law exemplified in the feather of the bird, in the limb of the horse, in the stem of wheat. Surely it was no fanciful or overstrained feeling of devotion which tempted us to exclaim, as we looked around on the mountains, the woods, the straits, and on the magnificent structure, dimly shown by the eclipsed sun,

These are Thy glorious works, Parent of good!

Today, to the majority of travellers the Britannia Bridge comes as no more than a deep rumble in the small hours of the morning, as the Irish Mail goes through. It stands, an even greater monument to the labours of Robert Stephenson than his tomb in Westminster Abbey.

Between the two tubular bridges lay the most exposed and storm-swept section of the Chester and Holyhead Railway. The twin headlands of Penmaenmawr and Penmaenbach rose sheer from the sea, and of these Penmaenmawr was no mere headland, but a mountain towering up to 1,553 ft. The road that struggled over its steep slopes, high above the sea, had always been something of a terror in coaching days. Stephenson's plan was to carry the railway at low-level round the base of the cliffs from the Conway side until the actual promontory was reached. He wished to keep the tunnelling to a minimum, and the actual bore was less than one-quarter of a mile; but at the western end the line emerged where the great rocks receded a little, and a short viaduct was necessary, which at high tide is actually in the sea. It is a most thrilling and dramatic piece of railway, but the thrill of traversing it today is nothing to the hazards experienced during construction. The viaduct is at all times exposed to the full force of the sea, and during the October of 1846 a north-westerly gale did much damage.

Originally it was proposed to build a solid sea wall leading to the western end of the tunnel. The works, although well advanced, were breached by the sea, and much of the rubble

11

51   Penmaenmawr Viaduct and Tunnel

washed away. It was then that the open-viaduct was suggested. The piers were placed edgeways to the sea, and
spanned by cast-iron girders 42 ft. long. The contour of the
sea wall was altered; outworks were built on the beaches, to
break the sea, and diminish the tremendous force of the
waves. Piles were driven into the beach, for the purpose of
protecting the foundations, and so eventually after three
years of the most anxious toil, the sea wall and the approach
to the tunnel was completed. Many years later the London
and North Western Railway replaced the cast-iron arches,
by a viaduct of solid masonry—but still in the sea at high
tide. Such was the expense originally involved at Penmaenmawr that Stephenson afterwards estimated he would

have saved £25,000 to £30,000 by having a long tunnel through the solid rock of the headland. His experience led him to suggest that in future railway engineers should avoid the necessity of contending with the sea! So far as he himself was concerned, he expressed the view that if he had to do it again he would build an open viaduct with narrow piers, so as to allow the sea to break on an open beach instead of against the solid obstruction of a sea wall.

Robert Stephenson did not survive his father by many years. His dear wife had died in 1842, and the strain of the Mania years and of the tubular bridges had told heavily upon him. Succeeding to his father's great wealth his closest friends begged him to give up the most exacting of his tasks, and the Britannia Bridge was indeed the last of his great works in England. He was, however, engineer to even greater bridges in Canada and Egypt, and he became President of the Institution of Civil Engineers in 1855. He held that office for two years, and was succeeded by Joseph Locke, but to this lifelong friend fell the sorrowful task of delivering from the Presidential chair an oration on the death of Stephenson, in 1859. Locke was a fine and telling speaker in the House of Commons; but when it fell to him to speak to his fellow engineers, not only of Stephenson but of Brunel, who died within weeks of each other, his halting words were fraught with the deepest emotion. As they listened in awed silence few among that company could have thought that Locke, too, would follow them within a year.

I have still to describe some of the most beautiful of Brunel's work. On the South Devon line he, too, braved the hazards of a long sea wall, between Dawlish and Teignmouth; but it was in his bridges that Brunel displayed perhaps his greatest artistry (14). On the main line of the Great Western, between Paddington and Bristol, all the structures were exceedingly massive. One need only mention the Wharncliffe viaduct at Hanwell (60), the bridge at Chippenham, and the tremendous castellated façades of the Box tunnel (56). But west of Exeter the railway was taken through a sparsely populated countryside; the vast holiday traffic that has grown up in recent years was not foreseen, and the line was built with only a single track beyond Exeter. Speeds were not expected to be high; gradients were severe, and in taking the line across the many deep valleys encountered in Devon and Cornwall Brunel built the majority of the viaducts of timber (52, 53). The general prototype of this most picturesque form of construction was a bridge carrying a public road over the line between Twyford and Reading (12), but in the West Country the design was varied to suit the different types of foundation possible. Where there was solid ground to build on Brunel erected towers of solid masonry, and from the top of these timber struts spread out to carry the horizontal girders of the viaduct. But on many stretches, and particularly in the neighbourhood of Saltash the line was carried across tidal creeks, and there piles were driven down through the mud to the solid ground beneath. In some cases the mud reaches a depth of 70 ft., and with the railway carried about 100 ft. above high-water mark the total height of the "legs" can well be appreciated. From almost any viewpoint the viaducts looked so slender that it was difficult to imagine them carrying anything so substantial as a train; actually they carried the entire main line traffic in Cornwall until 1908!

While the design of these bridges reflects the genius of Brunel, in the skilful use of timber, and the careful thought he had given to make them relatively easy to maintain, what captures the imagination even more, perhaps, is the craftsmanship developed by the viaduct gangs in dealing with repairs and renewals. The bridges were so designed that any piece of timber could be removed without affecting the rest of the structure. In carrying out this work the bridgemen would sit in bowline loops at the end of the ropes, working maybe, at a height of 100 ft. above the valley. If they wished to move they could swing themselves several feet sideways to the work without any assistance from those at the upper end of the rope. The old-fashioned yellow pine that Brunel used had an extraordinarily long life, and some sticks lasted in key positions for upwards of forty-five years. In later days every viaduct was thoroughly examined four times a year, when every timber would in turn be examined, and all bolts oiled. The entire freedom from accident, both to maintenance men and to the traffic on

52, 53   The replacing of two viaducts on the Falmouth line:
Ponsanooth (*above*) and Carnon (1862)

Brunel's Timber Viaducts

54   Construction in

55   On the sea w;
Both fr

THE SOUTH DEVON LI

progress near Totnes

.pproaching Teignmouth
ontemporary water-colours

N "ATMOSPHERIC" DAYS

56   Box: western end

57   St. Anne's Park: western end

58   Fox's Wood, beside the River Avon, near Keynsham
I. K. Brunel, engineer; all from drawings by J. C. Bourne, 1846

TUNNELS ON THE GREAT WESTERN

these bridges is a tribute to the training and experience of the gangs in question. The viaducts were in fact, not entirely free from accident, for on one occasion two goods trains met head-on in the middle of a lofty span. The timbers not merely withstood the tremendous shock of this collision, but the parapets prevented engines and trucks falling into the river below!

Brunel proposed to cross the Tamar by a timber bridge. His first design included for seven river spans, a central one of 250 ft. and three on either side, each of 100 ft. It would have been a magnificent specimen of a timber viaduct, though one that would not have carried modern traffic. It was fortunate for Brunel's successors that the Admiralty would not accept the design; otherwise they would have been faced with the task of building another great structure to replace it. Even so, when Brunel built the Royal Albert Bridge—one of the loveliest viaducts to be found on railways anywhere in the world—he provided only for a single line of rails (29, 30). It is pardonable that the present volume of holiday traffic into Cornwall was not foreseen at the time the bridge was built; but today it certainly constitutes a bottleneck, and when trains are out of course delays are often experienced, either at St. Budeaux or at Saltash. When the Prince Consort opened the bridge, on May 3rd, 1839, Brunel was not able to be present. His health had for some time been giving cause for anxiety. Although he was then only fifty-three years of age the terrible anxieties of his shipbuilding ventures had taken their toll, and he was abroad trying to regain his lost strength. He lived long enough to see the bridge completed, but only just. On his return to England he went down to Cornwall. He was too ill to walk, or stand, and a coach was placed on a trolley; and so, half sitting, half lying, he saw the great work which is the most abiding monument to his genius. Very slowly the trolley was drawn across the bridge. Some who looked on could scarcely believe that this frail weary man was the great Isambard Kingdom Brunel who they had known in the full vigour of his earlier, but not so very distant days on the Cornwall Railway. Three months later, on September 15th, 1859, he died.

Less than a month later Robert Stephenson also died, and

so it befell, on November 8th, that Joseph Locke spoke thus to the Institution of Civil Engineers:

> I cannot permit the occasion of opening a new session to pass without alluding to the irreparable loss which the Institution has sustained by the death, during the recess, of its two most honoured and distinguished members. . . .

He went on to speak with deep emotion, first of Brunel, and then of Stephenson, and then, in the oratory for which he was famous in Parliament he concluded:

> It is not my intention at this time to give even an outline of the works achieved by our two departed friends. Their lives and labours, however, are before us; and it will be our own fault if we fail to draw from them useful lessons for our own guidance. Man is not perfect, and it is not to be expected that he should always be successful; and, as in the midst of success we sometimes learn great truths before unknown to us, so also we often discover in failure the causes that frustrate our best directed efforts. Our two friends may probably form no exception to the general rule; but, judging by the position they had each secured, and by the universal respect and sympathy which the public has manifested for their loss, and remembering the brilliant ingenuity of argument, as well as the more homely appeals to their own long experience, often heard in this hall, we are well assured that they have not laboured in vain.
>
> We, at least, who are benefited by their successes, who feel that our Institution has reason to be proud of its association with such names as Brunel and Stephenson, have a duty to perform; and that duty is, to honour their memory and emulate their example.

Locke himself probably constructed more miles of railway in Great Britain than any other engineer. His work in France has already been mentioned, and he also introduced railways into Spain. But apart from the surveying of routes, and the eventual carrying through of the works, his name will always be associated with that particularly British institution, the bull-head rail. He used it first on the Grand Junction. In cross-section it was shaped roughly like a dumb-bell, with head and tail of equal size. Originally the intention was to turn it upside down after wear had taken place on the head, and so make it yield a double length of life; but in practice it was found that the battering received from the constant passage of traffic ruined the lower surface where it rested on the chairs, and the idea of turning was given up. Then the bull-head rail instead of being made with equal head and tail was re-designed so as to have a very much more massive head. In this form Locke's rail was virtually standard on all the railways of Great Britain for upwards of a hundred years; the Great Western used Brunel's "bridge" rail until the end of the broad gauge, in 1892, but the bull-head rail became standard afterwards.

By comparison with "the great triumvirate", as they have been called—Stephenson, Brunel, and Locke—Charles Vignoles was a most unlucky engineer. Although he always seemed to be in the thick of events, engaged on countless consultations and proposals, when events finally came to the point he was out-manœuvred, or just the victim of his own enthusiasm. I have told already of his association with the Liverpool and Manchester Railway, with the proposals for the Irish Mail route, and how, characteristically, he put tremendous enthusiasm into the backing of one of the losers in the Rainhill locomotive trials. It was fortunate for him that the débâcle of the Manchester and Sheffield line was followed so soon by the Railway Mania, when the services of all engineers were in such exceptional demand. One such project was the North Kent line the plans for which had to be deposited in the Parliamentary offices by November 30th, 1845. It was a terrible race against time, on which an extract from his diary throws a vivid light:

Some of us were engaged on the various plans and sections for twenty four hours at a time. Indeed for several nights not one of my staff went to bed. Many of them were completely knocked up. My son, Hutton, twenty-one years of age, on the last night of our work fell into a profound sleep with all his clothes on; and, as he could not be awakened, they cut off his Wellington boots, and rolled him into bed just as he was!

When the Mania was still running in full blast, Vignoles received an invitation that seemed to open the way to one of the most glittering prizes the railway world had yet offered, namely to examine and report upon a railway system for India. The invitation came from the East India Company, and Vignoles was to conclude a three years agreement to make the basic plan. It would, of course, have imposed upon him severe restrictions as to what other consultative work could be done at the same time, and some idea of the earnings of railway engineers in the Mania years can be gathered from the fact that Vignoles told the East India Company that he could not accept a salary of less than £7,000 per annum, with all expenses paid—in the year 1846, be it noted! But the most the East India Company was prepared to offer was £4,000, and so all negotiations were broken off, so far as Vignoles was concerned. In later years he built several foreign railways, including the Western Railway of Switzerland, and the Bilbao and Tudela Railway, in Spain, while his son Henry constructed the Isle of Man Railway. His successful engineering of the large suspension bridge over the Dnieper, at Kiev, and the high esteem in which he was held by the Imperial Government, following the completion of this work, seemed to be leading towards his employment in large-scale railway construction schemes in Russia. But the Crimean War put an end to any such negotiations, and by then Vignoles was gradually assuming the role of one of the elder statesmen of the engineering profession. Although his life had included so many disappointments, hazards and setbacks, he had lost neither his early zeal, nor his good health, nor yet that charm and courtesy of manner that even in the toughest of professional encounters made him the most chivalrous of opponents. In 1869, when in his seventy-sixth year, he was elected to the highest distinction any engineer can wish to attain, the Presidency of the Institution of Civil Engineers.

The most abiding monument to his work is the Vignoles rail. This, while having a head similar to Locke's rail had a broad flat bottom. As such it was particularly attractive to those railways who did not wish to incur the expense of the chairs needed to carry the bull-head rail. It could be laid flat on to the sleepers, and just spiked down, and while the bull-head was used in this country, on certain lines in India, and on the old État system in France—successor to the Rouen and Havre lines built by Locke—the Vignoles rail

59   The Skew Bridge at Bath

60   Wharncliffe Viaduct, near Hanwell
I. K. Brunel, engineer; both from drawings by J. C. Bourne, 1846

VIADUCTS ON THE GREAT WESTERN

61 William Cubitt, engineer of the South Eastern and of the Great Northern Railway

From an old photograph

62 C. B. Vignoles

From a painting at the time of his presidency of the Institution of Civil Engineers

came to be used nearly everywhere else in the world. Now, indeed, the wheel is coming almost completely full circle as the Nationalised British Railways are adopting the flat-bottomed, or Vignoles rail, for their future standard. There are refinements, since the early days of spiking down to the sleepers, as in modern practice, a baseplate, or "chair" is used between the rail and the timber. But in all essentials our most modern permanent way is being laid with the Vignoles rail. As to its designer, while his great contemporaries all died in middle age, he lived on, hale and hearty, with his keen intellect unimpaired to the age of eighty-three. His biography was written not by either of the sons who followed him as engineers, but by the third son, Olinthus, who was a clergyman; but in concluding this chapter, with its memories of Vignoles, may I refer to one of the greatest single engineering feats of our own time, the third Woodhead Tunnel.

I have referred earlier to the circumstances in which it became necessary to abandon the first tunnel, which Locke built, and the companion one alongside, built a very few years after the completion of the first. One might have thought that with the old tunnels alongside, and with all the experience of a hundred years of civil engineering, the driving of the third would have been a thoroughly straightforward project. Moreover, Locke's resident engineer, W. A. Purdon, had made a large and detailed longitudinal section along the original tunnels and through the five shafts. It described the strata encountered, named the fossils, and indicated the limits and locations of the geological features. With some thought for posterity this invaluable document had been deposited with the Geological Museum, South Kensington. As I have shown earlier in this book, many of the troubles experienced by the pioneer railway engineers were due to striking unexpected strata both in cuttings and in tunnelling, and a survey so close to the route to be followed by the new tunnel at Woodhead was an unusual gift for an engineer. But the men of 1949 ran into the most serious and unexpected difficulties, and even with all the modern plant at their disposal the third Woodhead Tunnel took four and a half years to complete, more than a year longer than the time

12

originally set as a target. In reading of the troubles experienced in the years 1950 and 1951 one could only feel more admiration than ever for the pioneers working under Locke who drove so deeply into the "unknown" beneath the Pennines, and completed the first tunnel in six years.

In the third Woodhead Tunnel the contractor planned to drive a pilot tunnel 12 ft. high and 12 ft. wide from each portal, and from a central shaft. Then, the procedure was to enlarge this small tunnel to the full size required by a series of carefully planned sequential operations. Under the older method of working the solid rock face was attacked: holes were drilled for the explosive charges, the charges were inserted and blown, and then all the debris had to be cleared away before the next drilling and exploding could be done. On the other hand, working from a small pilot tunnel it was intended to drill out radially; then the drillers could move on ahead, while the next gang packed the charges and fired them, and they in turn would be followed by the "mucking" gang who cleared away the debris. Progress was expected to be rapid, as by working as planned each gang could proceed continuously, without waiting for the succeeding to follow up and do their share, as when face drilling is used. Alas for such preparations! The nature of the rock proved such that the blasting operations blew a ragged and uncontrollable section; too much, or too little came away, and while the shaly nature of the rock contributed much to this disappointing result, the general opinion formed as a result of the experience at Woodhead was that radial drilling did not offer the chances of success anywhere.

The whole system of working had to be reorganised, and the revised plan had hardly got going when there came an accident as dramatic as anything experienced by the great pioneers of 120 years ago. Working inward from the Woodhead end of the tunnel, at about 800 ft. from the portal, the rock begins to change from hard sandstones and gritstones to shale. This portion of the tunnel was in process of enlargement from the pilot to full size in 1951, and erection of massive steel ribs to support the 31-ft. wide crown was proceeding. Then it was noticed that some of these ribs were showing signs of deflections; pieces of rock began to drop between the packings, the ribs began to distort at the crown, and the whole situation began to look very ugly. It was judged to be much too dangerous to try and put in additional supports; all men were withdrawn from the affected area, and just before midnight on the same day the whole roof collapsed, with the steel ribs crumpling up like so many lengths of copper wire! The tunnel was completely blocked for a length of 72 ft., so seriously indeed that it took six months to clear the debris. It was eventually discovered that a wedge-shaped cavity extending to a height of 70 ft. above the floor of the tunnel had formed as a result of this fall. So it went on. Throughout the work the third Woodhead Tunnel was a constant and changing battle against the forces of nature, which completely defeated the methodical plan worked out for the progress of the work. Nature, indeed, defied some of the best civil engineers of the "nineteen-fifties" just as violently as she defied Robert Stephenson at Penmaenmawr, and in Kilsby Tunnel, and Locke on this very same Sheffield line, and at Fareham.

CHAPTER V

Running the Trains

B Y the year 1850 the comprehensive railway system that was to serve this country was rapidly taking shape. Many trunk lines were in operation; great civil engineering obstacles like the Menai Straits, and the Pennine Range at Woodhead had been successfully mastered, while steam locomotives had passed far beyond the early experimental stages. Speeds of 60 m.p.h. and more were run as a matter of course by the broad gauge expresses of the Great Western. Everywhere traffic was on the increase, and with the greater number of trains in motion accidents were frequent. While most of these were of a minor character the potentialities for dire disaster were growing. Hitherto the heat and burden of the day had been borne by the young men of the profession. At the opening of the Liverpool and Manchester Railway George Stephenson alone was in middle age; not only in active participation, but in consultation the older men stood aside. The one outstanding exception was Nicholas Wood, who with his great influence and experience, and wise counsel must have been a tower of strength to Stephenson and his assistants. One can well imagine how the pioneer work of excavating great cuttings, bridging wide ravines and estuaries, and tunnelling fired the enthusiasm of the adventurous young spirits of the day. It was the same with early locomotive engineering: the urge to go faster than man had ever travelled before! That they all had moments, even months, of the gravest anxiety we know, but the prizes to be won were glittering.

But while the civil engineers were taking the lines through places which a few years earlier would have been thought completely impossible, and the mechanical engineers were building bigger, better and faster locomotives, a problem was very gradually, imperceptibly, yet inexorably looming up that was to beset the railways of this country throughout the nineteenth century, and is by no means solved today. It can be summed up in the one word "operation". Because it grew up so gradually, and with infinite variations on the different lines it was tackled piecemeal. No single-minded genius saw, or could have been expected to see the extent of the problem that was arising; nor was it entirely one of engineering. Moreover, the gradualness of the onset of the problem, as the speed and density of the traffic increased meant that officers that already held posts of major responsibility on the various railways dealt with the first pin-pricks of the operational "headache" as minor details in the course of their normal duties. They took the shortest cuts to the problems immediately presenting themselves; it would have been surprising if they had the time— let alone the inclination to take an altogether longer and broader view. So it befell to men who were, for the most part, outside the railway service to make the greatest contributions to the art of operation. In addition to the manufacturers of specialised types of apparatus the inspecting officers of the Board of Trade played a most noteworthy part. From time immemorial Government Officials of any kind have been a butt for every wit who wanted to raise a laugh; but through what might be termed the "middle-ages" of railway development in this country, the clear-sighted way in which these inspectors kept the whole picture in mind, while local railwaymen were naturally absorbed with their own particular trials and tribulations, had the salutary effect of keeping a measure of co-ordination at a very difficult time.

One could hardly find a better example of how chaotically things can get out of hand than the ceremonial opening day of the Liverpool and Manchester Railway. The operating arrangements for the day were entrusted to Locke(18), and with his usual care and forethought all had been worked out on a neat and orderly plan. Had everything run strictly according to that plan all would have been well; but on that very first day there were revealed, tragically, the unpredictable actions of passengers, the need for adequate brakes, and the need for a very complete system of communications. All these are vital factors to be taken into account in the running of trains, and that first day, exceptional though it was, could be taken as symbolical of difficulties to come. At the start all went well. Vignoles records in his diary:

Vast crowds had assembled from a very great distance but there was no confusion, as the arrangements were excellent.

There were eight special trains to convey the guests in a ceremonial procession from Liverpool to Manchester and back; the first was the State Car, conveying the Duke of Wellington and his suite, while the others followed. Each train was drawn by an engine of Stephenson's build, while the first six were driven by senior engineers of the company. They came in the following order:

Engine	Driver
"Northumbrian"	George Stephenson
"Phoenix"	Robert Stephenson (junr.)
"North Star"	Robert Stephenson (senr.)
"Rocket"	Joseph Locke
"Dart"	Thos. L. Gooch
"Comet"	William Allcard
"Arrow"	F. Swanwick
"Meteor"	A. Harding

Vignoles comments:

The procession started at twenty minutes to eleven o'clock. The brilliance of the cortege, the novelty of the sight, considerations of the almost boundless advantages of the stupendous power about to be put into operation, gave to the spectacle an unparalleled interest.

At one time the speed of the train in which Vignoles was travelling reached 24 m.p.h., but then came the stop to take water at Parkside. From eye-witness accounts it is a little difficult to appreciate exactly how it all came about, but apparently Mr. Huskisson, M.P. for Liverpool, was travelling in a different train to the Duke of Wellington, and when the stop came he climbed down and crossed the line to speak to the Duke. Various other guests did the same, and a number of them were on the line of railway when it was seen that the *Rocket* was approaching with the fourth train. Something of a panic ensued, as the guests tried to get to one carriage or another. Locke, who was driving the *Rocket*, must have seen all this ahead of him, and although no doubt he was slowing down he could not stop in time, and Mr. Huskisson, who seems to have lost his head, was run over. He was so seriously injured that he died the same evening. Such a tragedy cast a deep gloom over the proceedings, in fact the Duke of Wellington wished to abandon the whole programme there and then. But it was pointed out to him that a great number of people was awaiting his arrival in Manchester; his non-arrival would set the wildest rumours afoot, and eventually he agreed to proceed. One can imagine the inner feelings of the Stephensons, and especially of Locke, that such a thing had happened on this great day to which they had all looked forward; but any feelings of tragedy were quickly pushed aside by the practical necessity of getting the special trains through.

In Manchester the Duke was detested by the majority for his political opinions, and the tardy arrival of the state carriage was greeted with boos, cat-calls, insults and an occasional brick-bat. But this experience was nothing to what Robert Stephenson had to endure with the second special train. At a point about three miles out of Manchester, following the passage of the Duke's train a great crowd had surged over the railway, and Robert Stephenson on the *Phoenix* had literally to drive through the mob. Brick-bats were thrown; men swarmed up on to the carriages, and the rest of the journey was made with almost as many people hanging on outside as were ensconced inside. The procession which had started from Liverpool in such stately fashion straggled into Manchester as best it could, arriving about three o'clock. The reception from the crowd was so hostile that no one seems to have partaken of the state lunch that was provided, and operating arrangements on the railway seem at first to have centred upon the urgent necessity of getting the Duke back to Liverpool. It was now that things began to get completely out of hand, and the need for a good system of communications became so apparent. A special train for the Duke left about four o'clock, but after that nobody seemed to know quite what was happening, or who was where! The plain fact remained, that at five o'clock the majority of the guests were still in Manchester; twenty-four

coaches were available to convey them, but only three locomotives. The Duke's special would account for one more,
while earlier in the day yet another had been used to rush
Mr. Huskisson to where he could receive medical attention.
Where the remaining three locomotives were is not recorded.

The twenty-four carriages were duly marshalled into one
long train, and the three available engines were coupled on
in front. Dusk was falling before they left Manchester, but
although most of the crowds along the line had dispersed by
that time, there were fresh hazards to be faced on the long
journey back to Liverpool. The engines themselves were
overloaded, but in places where people had swarmed over the
line the rails were in a foul condition, with mud trampled
over the running surfaces. All the engines concerned had
but a single pair of driving wheels, and the state of the rails
led to much slipping. In any case the pull necessary to keep
those twenty-four coaches on the move set up excessive
stresses in the drawbars of the leading vehicles; a coupling
broke, and a rope was substituted! Progress continued to be
desperately slow, and the thoughts of those on the locomotives must have been directed ahead as to what would happen
when they reached the Whiston incline, with its mile of
1 in 91 ascent. Things were bad enough on the level! Fortunately, however, two further engines were coming eastwards,
feeling their way in the darkness, to meet the long trundling
cavalcade; they were duly coupled up, and the five engines
then duly essayed the climb. Such were the conditions,
however, that the load very nearly overpowered the lot of
them, and it was only after an appeal to all male passengers
to get out and walk that the crest of the bank was reached.
What a day it must have been for those responsible, and not
least for the guests who were not delivered back in Liverpool
until nearly ten o'clock at night. Yet of those engineers who
took part, all seem to have made light of the difficulties; any
hazards, setbacks, and delays were regarded as mere incidents
compared with the prospects opened up by the inauguration
of the railway.

In writing of railway engineers in the later part of the
Victorian age, if one were to treat the various facets of
operation in the chronological order that the more significant

events took place, the result would be a very long and rather disjointed narrative; and for much of the time it might be difficult to discern just where events were leading us. I have chosen, therefore, instead to sketch in a rather broad picture of the problem as a whole, as it had developed in nearly a hundred years of railway working, and then turn the limelight upon the milestones and the men most deeply concerned. In the inauguration of railway transport the major efforts and interests were concentrated upon the track and the motive power; for without a good track and formation railways would have advanced little beyond the old wagon-ways, and without steam locomotives there would have been no development worth the name. Today, while the track is still the foundation of all things, and the capacity of locomotive is often well extended in the handling of heavy and fast trains, it is equally true to say that in many districts the traffic just could not be worked without the elaborate arrangements of signalling that are provided. Trains follow each other very closely; drivers require immediate warning if the line ahead is not clear, but again the most elaborate system of signalling would be useless if the trains were not provided with adequate brakes. The faster the trains, the better should be the brakes; yet while this might seem obvious enough the development of braking systems for many years lagged far behind the increasing capacity for speed built into succeeding designs of locomotives. In comparatively recent years the maximum speed of a new British streamlined train had to be limited to 70 m.p.h. over one of the finest pieces of road in the country, because the brakes were not powerful enough to stop the train within the warning distances given by the signals. And yet the locomotive could have hauled that train at 100 m.p.h., if need be.

In the earliest days there was need to tell engine-drivers where to stop, and policemen were stationed at intervals along the line. They gave signs by raising their arms; but even with the low speeds run it was soon found necessary to use mechanical devices to give the required signals, since these could be mounted on high masts and seen from a greater distance away. Many and various were the shapes of these early signals, but at the very start railway signalling on most lines in this country commenced on what proved to be a faulty principle: that no signal at all meant "all clear". The various discs, semaphores, or boards were turned edge-on, or otherwise disappeared from view when conditions were safe for the train to proceed. At night, while "red" was the signal for danger, "white" signified "all clear". The risk inherent in such a principle is clear enough today, but was evidently not appreciated then. The signal arm, or disc might collapse, or be blown away, and then it would be almost impossible for the driver of a train approaching fast to distinguish whether it was really there—edge on. At night the red glass might be broken and fall away, leaving the white light of the lamp showing, and falsely indicating "all clear". Still, the colours were at first traditional, and bitter experience alone was to cause a change to be made. Green was used on some early railways as a caution signal. The Great Western and the Southampton used definite signs for clear; but they were in a minority. Even after the death of Mr. Huskisson, brakes remained entirely primitive for several decades.

The need for warning drivers of the routes set at junctions was realised at an early stage in railway history, and a so-called "light-house" was erected at Corbett's Lane, Bermondsey, where the "Atmospheric" line to Croydon joined the London and Greenwich Railway. When the points were set for a train to take the Croydon line a large red-orange disc was displayed, and a red light at night; for a Greenwich train the disc was turned on edge, so as to show nothing, and a white light was shown at night. Even for those early days that "red" proceed indication for the Croydon trains was a questionable point, and when the line was inspected by the Board of Trade prior to opening the Government Inspector gave a rather grudging approval. Although there was a definite timetable for the trains on both routes it was thought necessary to provide some distinguishing mark on the Croydon trains to distinguish them from the Greenwich ones, so that the pointsman at Corbett's Lane Junction could set the road accordingly. Here again the indications were partly negative, in that Greenwich trains carried no identification at all. Croydon trains carried two white lights, one above the other, on the front of the engine at night, while in the day-time a red ball was hung out by the conductor on the leading coach. Thus again there was a possibility of mistaken signals; for if the lights had gone out, or if the ball fell off its carrier, a Croydon train could be taken for one bound for Greenwich.

The earliest engine-drivers were picked men, chosen for their sense of responsibility; but as railways extended it was perhaps inevitable that some of those put in charge of loco-motives proved less reliable. A vivid light upon railway operating conditions in the early "forties" is thrown by an accident that occurred at Nine Elms, when one train ran into the back of another, at night. In his report to the Board of Trade Sir Frederic Smith discussed the question of pro-viding tail lights on trains. But he added: "It may, however, be doubted whether any light would have aroused the atten-tion of the engineman or his fireman who, I suspect, must have been in a state of great drowsiness; and the question naturally arises what would have been the most effective way of drawing the attention of men under such circum-stances, or in foggy weather." At that very early date in railway history he had, indeed, touched upon the ever-present problem of how to alert a driver who through care-lessness, or some temporary distraction on his engine is running past signals at caution or danger. It is possible, though not certain that the most terrible accident in recent times—the double collision at Harrow in 1952—arose from this very same cause.

In his report of 1840 Sir Frederic Smith refers to the so-called "puppets" erected by Edward Bury, the locomotive superintendent, on the London and Birmingham Railway. They were fixed to the rail at the place where it was required to attract the attention of the enginemen, or guard of the train. As the engine passed it touched a lever by which a steam whistle was sounded, and a red light which was carried on the engine was turned so that it shone full in the face of the driver! The red light remained with them, as if to say: "You have been warned." Little is known of this device. It probably had many mechanical faults, but it remains of out-standing historical interest, as being one of the first, if not the first attempt to give engine-drivers something in addition to the wayside signals when caution was needed. The inventor, Edward Bury, for some time held a rather curious position in the railway world, in that he was at one and the same time locomotive superintendent of one of the largest railways, the London and Birmingham, and also the proprietor of a locomotive manufacturing business. His dual role, lent itself to many complications, particularly as he had rather decided views on locomotive design. The tiny little four-wheeled engines that he built in his own works were excellent little things in themselves, but they were, even by the early "forties", inadequate for the London and Birmingham. In his continued recommendation of the type he came eventually under suspicion, and had to resign; but he deserves a place in the gallery of the pioneers, if for no other reason than his invention of the earliest form of cab signalling. The astonishing similarity of his device to arrangements that were extensively used later will be apparent when this particular story reaches the "nineties" of last century.

Apparently it was not long before something more elaborate than the original "light-house" was needed at the junction of the Greenwich and Croydon lines. Tall semaphores were proposed; but then Mr. C. H. Gregory, engineer to the line at the time, decided to concentrate the control of all the junction signals in one place. The signals were operated by means of stirrups into which the man placed his foot; the stirrups were all mounted in a single row, and to give the "policeman" a better view up and down the line the frame was mounted on an elevated platform. This installation was brought into service in 1843, and it was, indeed, the father of all signal boxes. Gregory devised the arrangement as part of his duties as civil engineer, and although, when seen in retrospect, it was a piece of pioneer railway work comparable in ultimate importance with the locomotive blast pipe or the Vignoles rail, he seems to have attached little significance to it. Sir Charles Gregory, as he afterwards became, was President of the Institution of Civil Engineers in the year preceeding Vignoles's year of office. It is customary for the President in his address to the Institution to dwell upon important phases of his own career; but one searches in

vain through Gregory's address for any mention of the
signal lever frame on the Croydon Railway. He was far more
concerned with armaments: firearms, armour-plated ships,
and the urgent need for erecting forts in the seaward
approaches to our great ports; and he stressed the importance
of railways as a means of concentrating troops rapidly to
meet a sudden emergency. That was in 1868, when the
experiences of the Crimean War were still fairly fresh to
mind, and when railways had played a considerable part
in the American Civil War.

His other references to railways have an odd ring today,
and are worth quoting. The first flush of enthusiasm had
long faded away, and those who had invested in railways
were mostly disappointed at not receiving a greater return
on their capital. Gregory commented as follows:

> At a time when so much criticism is directed to the manage-
> ment and effects of Railway Enterprise it should not be for-
> gotten how much of the present evil has arisen from unprofit-
> able works forced on Companies by public opinion, and from
> the freedom with which Parliament has sanctioned competing
> lines. . . .
>
> While many Railway Companies are suffering from the effects
> of the unproductive outlay of capital on branch lines, it may
> be well to remember the special benefits which that outlay has
> conferred on the landowners and inhabitants of the country
> traversed, benefits which the people of many districts at present
> unserved by railways must be anxious to possess, but for which
> it is clear that the necessary capital cannot now be furnished by
> private enterprise. It would appear, then, to be a favourable
> time for reconsidering the principle of constructing local lines
> by means of rates to be levied on the districts which would be
> more directly benefited by their construction.

Today, more and more of these branch lines are being
closed down. Although many of them are so little used by
the inhabitants there is usually an outcry when the notice
of closure is published; but local sentiment does not always
rise to the pitch of fever heat immortalised by the exploits
of *The Titfield Thunderbolt!*

Some of the mechanisms used for actuating the early railway semaphores were marvels of ingenuity. F. D. Banister,

the engineer of the Brighton Railway, designed a form of double semaphore mounted on a single post. The arms, which pointed outwards, worked from a common pivot, but could be independently controlled—since one of the semaphores related to the down line and the other to the up. These signals were a development of one of the earliest form of railway semaphore; in the latter the arm had to disappear completely from view when the line ahead was clear, and so the signals were made to work in a slot in the post. In the Banister signals on the Brighton line the slot was made wide enough to accommodate two semaphores, though the clear indication was given when the arm was inclined downwards. The slot in the post died hard! The North Eastern Railway used it right down to the time of grouping, in 1923, although the idea of the disappearing arm had been abandoned on that line for over seventy years! The method of mounting was complicated and costly, yet by tradition it remained. But tradition was surely carried beyond nearly all reason on the North Eastern when some lattice iron signals were erected at Newcastle in 1906, and *these* were made with a central gap and mountings for the semaphore. Mention of lattice iron posts, however, brings me to one of the names that will live forever in signalling history. While Bury had designed his early locomotive cab signalling, and while C. H. Gregory and Banister had each made contributions, signalling became the work of a lifetime for John Stevens.

Stevens began his working life as a blacksmith in Southwark; he made pickaxes and shovels, and forged swords that were used at the Battle of Waterloo. With the coming of railways he was keen enough to realise that a new field for wrought-iron accessories was opening up, and in due course he and his sons set up a business for the special purpose of making signal equipment. With some ingenuity they called their small establishment in Southwark the "Darlington Works". Stevens had the rare knack of attracting the right kind of men to his service, and although the various innovations that came from the firm were known as "Stevens" products it was, in particular the three members of the Deakin family who between them produced some of the cleverest inventions. Some twenty-five years ago, as a

young engineer myself, I came to know W. H. Deakin, son
of one of those pioneer inventors, and with many others
listened enthralled to his tales of the old days. His father
had joined Stevens in 1844, while he himself began work
there in 1863. It was Deakin's father who invented the
lattice iron type of signal post, designed to supersede timber,
and by its open construction to offer less resistance to the
wind. It would, I think, be true to say that tens of thousands
of these posts have been made, for service on railways all
over the world.

While "Stevens and Sons" were well established as the
first signalling firm in the world, another potential inventor
of great versatility was working as a mechanic on the
Brighton Railway under F. D. Banister; his name was John
Saxby (65). One of his earliest efforts—and a little master-
piece it was!—concerned the oil-lamps for the two-arm
Banister signals. The semaphores related to the opposing
directions of traffic, and were distinguished by different
painting on the face and back of the arms; but Saxby contrived that a single oil-lamp should provide the night indications for both directions of running, by having two revolving
tables inside the lamp case, one connected to the one semaphore arm and one to the other, and these tables carried the
glasses necessary for producing the night indications of the
signal. Though not fundamental in any way it was a very
clever mechanism, but it proved the forerunner of further
inventions that were to lay the foundations of modern
signalling practice. The name of Saxby, no less than those
of Deakin, and Stevens & Sons, will always be associated
with the great art of interlocking, and it is now necessary to
explain its vital function.

The early signals erected along the railways and at
junctions, could be operated at will. Reliance was placed
upon the "policeman" or pointsman working to the rules
laid down. Many of these men were, however, completely
illiterate, and as the density of traffic grew the responsibility
placed upon them began to exceed their capacity. At a much
later date the old handicap of illiteracy had vanished and a
fine type of man was to be found in signal boxes; but just as
the moderate "rush" periods of the "fifties" taxed the early

policeman, so the greatly increased business of the "eighties" and "nineties" taxed their successors. There were always chances of a serious mistake being made when the man was hard pressed, and safety devices were necessary to guard against such slips in working. A signalman might, for example, set the points and clear the signals for one route, and in a moment of forgetfulness set up a conflicting route on which the two trains could collide. Gregory's stirrup frame did not include any device to prevent a wrong route being signalled; indeed the necessity for having some form of safeguard was not expressed until sixteen years later, when Colonel Yolland, one of the inspecting officers of the Board of Trade was examining the equipment provided for Kentish Town Junction on the North London Railway. He then asked the engineer, one Austin Chambers, to include some mechanism whereby conflicting signals could not be shown for diverging and converging routes. The sequel provided a classic for all time in the history of railway signalling. The story has been told many times before, but it will bear telling again.

A mechanism was duly devised, and Colonel Yolland was invited to come and see it. He was shown that if the main line signal was lowered, it was impossible to lower that for the branch; while a further demonstration showed that the converse was also true. But instead of giving the expected Government blessing the Colonel stepped forward, and manœuvred his foot so as to get it into both stirrups at once; then, pressing his foot down, to everyone's horror he lowered both signals at once! This test, completely outside the rules of the game so to speak, acted as a spur and a challenge to railway engineers. They were put on their mettle against the unexpected, the unpremeditated, and from that time onwards a system of elaborate safeguards was gradually worked out to cover many eventualities in railway operation. The ensuing years provided a feast, and no less a time of great anxiety for inventors. Every new device that appeared was patented, and unless a manufacturing firm could produce something different from that of their rivals they were liable to go out of business. It was in this game of "cut and thrust", among signal manufacturers that John Saxby established

63 "Hole in the Wall": an early signal-box at Victoria, equipped with Saxby signals and interlocking

64 George Westinghouse: inventor of the automatic air brake

65 John Saxby: signal and interlocking pioneer

such a reputation. His case had some semblance to that of James Watt in earlier years, in that he, a clever inventor, was fortunate enough to enlist as partner a wealthy man with a fine business accumen. The firm of Saxby and Farmer dates from 1856, and in that year Saxby carried the original Gregory idea of a row of actuating members a stage further by including point levers with the signal levers. Saxby himself seems to have been a "rough diamond", and he was as forthright in his dealings with railway officers as he was ruthless in competition with his rivals. Lawsuits for infringement of patent was frequent, and the names of Easterbrook, Tate, Jeffrey, and Rapier occur many times in the stormy history of the early interlocking machines.

Although Stevens was earliest in the field he had not, at first, realised the importance of protecting every step by patent. The art of interlocking was still in its infancy when his firm installed a set of levers at Yeovil Junction, on the London and South Western Railway. Saxby had patented a new arrangement of levers, and on hearing of the Yeovil apparatus, and afterwards inspecting it, he brought an action against Stevens for infringement. To prove their case beyond any doubt Saxby and Farmer made a model of their type of apparatus, and their leading counsel, Mr. Bovil, Q.C., demonstrated the working of the interlocking in court. But Stevens was more than equal to the situation. The next day when the hearing was resumed the court assembled to find a large object in the centre, covered with a sheet. Their counsel duly removed the sheet to reveal the very interlocking frame that had been installed at Yeovil. Another had been installed in its place. Counsel had called Colonel Rich, one of the Board of Trade inspectors to appear as witness, and he now proceeded:

Counsel: Now, Col. Rich, I believe you officially inspected an interlocking appliance at Yeovil Junction on the S.W.R.?

Col. Rich: Yes, it was a new invention, and a very great step forward in the safe working of railways.

Counsel: Was it anything like that?, and he pointed to the lever frame displayed in court.

Col. Rich: Yes, as far as I can remember it was much like that.

Counsel: Well, I may tell you that that machine was the very

13

one you inspected at Yeovil Junction. Now can you give me
the date when you inspected that locking frame?

Colonel Rich produced a note-book, and after perusing it
for some time said: Yes, it was March 7th, 1860.

Counsel: Well, my Lord, I need only call your attention to the
date of complainant's patent, which was July 19th. 1860, so
that this supposed infringement was fixed and at work
some *four months* before the date of the patent.

W. H. Deakin used to tell with glee of the commotion that
ensued in that court, since the lengthy battle which had
lasted several months was ended thus in a few minutes and
cost Saxby and Farmer many thousands of pounds.

Many different patents for interlocking apparatus followed;
many were weirdly complicated (63), others no more than
partly successful, but when James Deakin, a cousin of
"W.H." brought out his great invention of the so-called
"tappet" locking, in 1870, Stevens and Sons made no mistake
about it, and it was patented at once. Like all really great
inventions it was extremely simple. While Saxby used
rocking mechanisms and grids, while the famous Worcester
firm of McKenzie and Holland used an ingenious, but complicated arrangement of cams, Deakin used a simple tappet,
or sword iron, engaging with a series of cross-members to
provide the necessary interlocking. In due course Deakin's
arrangement superseded all others. The merit of it could
not be more clearly shown than by the action of Saxby and
Farmer, on the one hand, and of McKenzie and Holland on
the other. The very moment the patent of Stevens expired
both those firms immediately introduced locking frames of
their own including the tappet method of interlocking.

At the time of Deakin's invention railway working was
still largely haphazard. Although the Board of Trade inspectors could "recommend" the companies were still not under
any statutory obligation to provide interlocking of signals
or points, and although it was no doubt an exaggeration Sir
John Tenniel's famous cartoon in *Punch* in 1872 reflected
something of the feeling of the times. The overworked
pointsman at "Muddleby Junction" ruminated thus:

Let's see! There's a 'scursion were due at 4.45 and it aint in
yet; then afore that, were the mineral—no, that must ha' been

the goods—or the cattle. No that were after, cattle's shuntin' now. Let's see! Fast train came through at—confound—and here comes the express afore its time, and blest if I know which line she's on.

It was not enough to have signals that could be clearly seen, and interlocking between signal and point levers at the larger stations; the flow of traffic needed to be properly regulated along the line. The invention of the electric telegraph put a most valuable instrument into the hands of railway engineers, though at first it was used for purposes other than the control of train movements. There was isolated exceptions. As early as 1841 on the North Midland Railway the telegraph was used to safeguard the passage of trains through the long tunnel near Clay Cross. Instead of using the earlier method of allowing a second train to proceed after a pre-arranged time had elapsed since the previous one had passed the policeman, working by space interval was inaugurated. A second train was not allowed to enter the Clay Cross tunnel until the previous one was reported, by telegraph, to be clear of the further end. This method of working is the basis of all modern British railway operating, whereby the line is divided up into a series of "block" sections. It will be remembered that George Stephenson was engineer to the North Midland Railway, and one may wonder if this method of "block" working through Clay Cross tunnel—so near to his home—was due to him. I have never seen it claimed on his behalf, and his faithful biographer does not mention it. But the man whose name will always be quoted with block telegraph working on railways is Edward Tyer, who was actively engaged in signalling invention over a period of sixty years—1850 to 1910. It was he who did more, perhaps, than any other man to develop the instruments used in signal boxes for transmitting the messages exchanged between adjacent boxes prior to the passage of a train. His firm, Tyer and Company, was founded in 1851, and today it is the oldest signalling firm in existence.

Hitherto, the men who had taken a leading part in the development of railways in this country were everyone of them British; but by the middle of the nineteenth century railways were spreading rapidly on the Continent of Europe, and in America, and for a brief time our scene changes to the Western side of the Atlantic. There, on the flanks of the Vermont mountains, a family that came of Westphalian stock had been settled for more than a hundred years; their name was originally Wistinghausen, but in the new world they changed it to an anglicised version, Westinghouse (64). Eighth of a young family of ten at the time of the American Civil War was a sturdy youth named George; he was not yet fifteen when war broke out, but he ran away from home to enlist in the Union Army, following thus in the footsteps of his elder brothers. At first his father intervened; but two years later he was allowed to go, and thus he was able to fulfil the ambition of the best American youth of the day, that of serving their country as an adventure, a privilege and a duty. It is perhaps not generally realised that in the Civil War more than 40 per cent of the enrolments in the Union Army were boys of eighteen and under. George Westinghouse's brother Albert, was killed leading a cavalry charge in 1864, and his brother John served in the navy. In 1865 George was demobilised, an officer, and yet not nineteen years of age; and he rejoined his father's small business in Schenectady, where agricultural machinery was made. How he came to be connected with railways is no part of the present story, but in 1869 he took out his first patent for a compressed air brake for trains. This was continuous throughout the train; connections were made from coach to coach by flexible pipes, and the movement of a single valve by the driver caused the brakes to be applied on every vehicle. It was widely adopted, almost at once, on the leading American railways, and Westinghouse was so heartened by this success that in 1871 he paid his first visit to Europe with a view to its introduction, both in Great Britain and on the Continent.

This was certainly a remarkable enterprise for a young man of twenty-five years of age; but in England at any rate, his reception was cool, to say the least of it. Just as George Stephenson, introducing the steam locomotive, had come up against the innate caution, conservatism, and prejudice of English business interests, so George Westinghouse encountered the same sympathies among the railway managements. In certain quarters the very fact that he was an American told against him. Others were, as yet, unconvinced of the need for any improvement. But if the official railway attitude was then negative Westinghouse was certainly not without sympathy in England. Men who could view railway development with a more detached outlook saw clearly that improvement was vitally necessary, and after several interviews with Westinghouse the well-known technical journal *Engineering*, published a leading article on the general subject of railway brakes, but with particular reference to the use of compressed air. That leading article went a great deal further than Westinghouse had done, for it stipulated two conditions of operation that, in the opinion of the journal were essential, thus: "If a part of the train breaks loose from the rest, the brakes must come automatically into play; the failure of the brake apparatus on one or more carriages must not interfere with the action of the brakes on the rest of the train." Westinghouse could not yet fulfil these requirements; but the precise specification thus laid down by a British technical journal undoubtedly put him on the track towards the great invention by which he will always be remembered. In less than a year he had filed his patents for the *automatic air brake*.

In the "straight air brake", as the earlier arrangement became known, the application of the driver's valve caused air to flow down the continuous pipe, and apply the brakes on each vehicle on the train. Thus if the pipe was fractured, or a portion of the train broke away that part beyond the point of failure would have no brakes. In the automatic brake the train pipe was kept charged with compressed air, and brakes were applied by a *reduction* of pressure, instead of an increase. It will be seen at once that such a system is inherently safe, as a leakage, or a breakaway would cause the brakes to be applied in both sections of the train. In addition to the train pipe Westinghouse provided a separate supply of compressed air on each vehicle in what is termed an auxiliary reservoir; and when the driver makes an application of the brakes, and the pressure of air in the train pipe is reduced a device called a triple valve, mounted on each vehicle, causes air to flow from the auxiliary reservoir to the cylinders used for applying the brakes. After a brake application the driver had to be sure the auxiliary reservoirs were fully charged again before he made a second application. There is no denying that it required considerable intelligence on the part of the driver; but the benefits to be derived in running the trains were such as to outweigh any additional training that was needed by the men.

The railways in Great Britain were certainly becoming a little more "brake conscious", after the visit of Westinghouse in 1871. A few trials were made of the straight air brake, but in the meantime numerous English inventors were entering the field, and between them some weird and wonderful contraptions were produced. Eventually it was arranged to stage some brake trials, and a stretch of the Nottingham–Lincoln line of the Midland Railway, near Newark, was chosen as the scene of action. One of those who had been more sympathetic to Westinghouse was William Stroudley, locomotive superintendent of the London, Brighton and South Coast Railway, and to the Newark trials of 1875 he sent an engine and train completely fitted up with the Westinghouse automatic air brake. Its efficacy was shown in the distances the various trains took to stop from an initial speed of 50 m.p.h.

Barker and Clark's hydraulic brake (G.E.R. train)	901 ft.
Smith's simple vacuum brake	1,477 ft.
Steel and McInnes air brake	1,158 ft.
Westinghouse automatic air brake	777 ft.

At these trials the London and North Western Railway had a train fitted with the Clarke and Webb chain brake; but it was a "gimcrack" thing, and gave erratic results in service.

The railway jubilee was celebrated in 1875—fifty years after the opening of the Stockton and Darlington line—and although great progress had been made in many directions, the operating methods on some of the principal main lines still left a great deal to be desired. Two fundamental weaknesses were emphasised in a disastrous collision at Abbots

Ripton on the Great Northern Railway in January 1876. On this line the block system was in operation, but in its earlier form. The signals stood normally in the clear position, and were put to danger after the passage of a train. When information was received by block telegraph that the train had passed the signal box next down the line the signals were restored to the clear position. Well, January 21st of that year was a very bad night of sleet and snow; but even so trains were running remarkably near to their booked time. The signals in the district south of Peterborough were all of the type working in a slot in the post, and the first evidence that things were going wrong came when a coal train for London ran past all the signals at Holme, a little station on the fringe of the fens. The signalman there had his levers at danger, as it was his intention to stop the coal train, and shunt it out of the way of the *Flying Scotsman* which was due soon afterwards. The men on the coal train engine were afterwards proved to be a very alert and responsible pair, and the signalman at Holme immediately telegraphed to Abbots Ripton information that the train had run through and was coming on towards him. Abbots Ripton lay some six miles to the south, and between that station and Holme were two intermediate signal boxes, Connington and Wood-walton. These were equipped with the block telegraph, but had no ordinary telegraph, so that they could not be informed of the run-through at Holme. There was, in any case, no point in stopping the train at either of these boxes, since there were no points and it could not be shunted.

The man at Abbots Ripton placed his signals to danger in readiness for stopping and shunting the coal train, but although the driver was aware that the Scotch Express was due, and he was slowing down, he was surprised to find the Abbots Ripton signals showing all clear. The signalman was very much on the alert after what happened at Holme, and by waving a red lamp from his cabin window there was no difficulty this time in warning the train. It was duly stopped; shunting back duly commenced, but not before the engine-men had warned the signalman that his signals were all showing a false clear. In actual fact snow had packed into the slot in the post, and accumulated on the arms, and the blades were all frozen in the clear position. The same happened at Woodwalton after the passage of the coal train. The signalman there put his levers back, but the frozen signals did not respond, and he did not seem to realise how dangerous conditions were becoming. He received advice on the block telegraph from Connington that the *Flying Scotsman* was approaching, but although it was snowing hard, and ice was packing up round the windows of the box he failed to carry out two precautions required by the rules, in case of falling snow or fog: to put detonators on the line, and to show a red lamp to the approaching train. He did neither, and when the *Flying Scotsman* came along its enginemen saw clear signals and continued at full speed. There was now scarcely a hope of avoiding a collision, and with the Abbots Ripton signals still showing false clear the express ran through, and crashed into the coal train as it was being shunted into the siding. Vehicles and debris were flung all over the place, and some piled up on the northbound main line.

The 5.30 p.m. express from Kings Cross to Leeds was approaching in the opposite direction, and the Abbots Ripton signalman was just too late to have it stopped, or warned with detonators as it passed Stukeley signal box; and so to the inadequacies of signalling arrangements was added a tragic demonstration of the inadequacy of the brakes. It might have been a great deal worse, but for the presence of mind of the coal train driver and fireman. They realised that the Leeds train was almost due, and the fireman ran down the line towards Huntingdon to put detonators on the northbound line; his driver followed him, with the engine, and although the signals on this line were also frozen they managed to warn the oncoming express, by whistling, showing a red lamp, and the explosion of the detonators. The train was travelling at about 45 m.p.h. and had about 1,000 yards in which to stop short of the debris; but the express had only the most primitive of brakes—hand brakes only, on the engine and tender, and in the two brake vans. The driver gave the emergency code on his whistle, and the two guards hearing it promptly put the brakes on in their respective vans; as a last resort the driver reversed his engine, and put full steam on, "in her teeth" so to speak. But it was of no avail, and at about 20 m.p.h. he crashed into the wreckage of the *Flying Scotsman*. In all thirteen persons were killed and twenty-four injured.

The prime cause of the accident was, of course, the freezing up of the actual signals; but with the method of working then used they remained a long time in the clear position. It was realised afterwards that if the method of block working was reversed, and the signals kept at danger till they were required to give passage to a train any freezing up would have been on the side of safety. Although the slotted ports came in for some criticism it was the system of block working that was fundamentally wrong, and this was changed afterwards to the method now standard on British Railways: the line is closed normally, and is opened for the passage of a train. There are today certain sections of automatically controlled colour light signals where this does not apply, but otherwise it is practically universal. As to the brakes, by that time many railwaymen were all too well aware of the need for vastly improved methods of working, but it must be recorded that the railway managements in Great Britain seemed disinclined to incur the expense, nor was there any sort of unanimity as to the best form of brake to adopt in the future. In the same way that civil engineers had dealt with the problems of signalling as they arose, so mechanical engineers dabbled—no more than dabbled, with the problem of improving brake power.

The glaring example of Abbots Ripton was not enough to rouse the consciousness of some administrations, and three years later we find Sir Richard Moon, the Chairman of the L. & N.W.R. extolling the chain brake as "the most perfect appliance that could be devised"; it was, of course, obvious to the merest amateur that the whole affair became inoperative if the chain broke! At this time the Board of Trade had a very difficult time of it. The inspecting officers saw clearly that sooner or later there ought to be one type of brake for all the railways in the country; that it should be automatic they were convinced beyond any doubt, yet some of the largest and most influential railways were persisting in the use of contrivances like the Clarke and Webb chain brake.

The "Brighton" decided on Westinghouse at an early date; the North Eastern followed suit in 1877, but among the larger railways the Midland was at first undecided, and in 1878 to 1880 they were experimenting with four different kinds of brake. Of these Smith's simple vacuum was frowned upon by the Board of Trade, and in any case it produced poor stops, while Barker's hydraulic brake, while giving reasonably good stops was liable to freeze up. The real competition was between the Westinghouse automatic, and the automatic vacuum, which had been devised by Sanders and Bolitho. The Westinghouse was regarded as an interloper, despite its excellent performance. So there developed the Battle of the Brakes. While this particular railway dog-fight did not reach to the extent of a Royal Commission, as the diverse gauges had done thirty-five years before, the battle was joined in some heat, and for the most part the technical conflict centred upon the Midland Railway.

At one time at least sixty Midland engines were fitted with the air brake, and it seemed likely that it would be adopted as standard. If that had happened it is quite possible that Westinghouse would have won over the whole of the British railways. The three largest Scottish railways had already decided; there were also the North Eastern and the Great Eastern. Had the Midland decided for Westinghouse the Great Northern as ally of the North Eastern and hemmed by "Westinghouse" railways on all sides could hardly have held out, and with the amount of inter-working at various points the hand of the London and North Western would almost certainly have been forced, however tardy and reluctant the ultimate decision might have been. At the same time, there is no doubt that the Midland locomotive department had a great regard for the automatic vacuum brake. For one thing it was much simpler to operate, and they continued development work; and it was just at this critical point that the Westinghouse interests in this country made a fatal step. The Midland having a supply of compressed air on their locomotives sought to use it for other purposes as well as braking, and an arrangement was designed for pneumatic sanding of the rails, to improve the grip of the wheels when starting, or in bad weather. For some reason that is difficult to appreciate after this lapse of time the Westinghouse Brake Company regarded compressed air on locomotives as there for the exclusive use of controlling the brakes, and they took the strongest exception to its use for sanding. Relations grew strained. The Midland re-doubled their efforts to perfect the automatic vacuum brake and very soon it was evident that Westinghouse had lost the day.

It is astonishing, however, to read some of the statements of railway chairmen and railway engineers on the subject of brakes in those difficult years. The fight that was put up in certain quarters for non-automatic brakes seems incredible to us now. Some railways, notably the Great Northern, and the Manchester, Sheffield and Lincolnshire seemed to delight in flaunting their open defiance of the Board of Trade, and the recklessness of statements that followed certain accidents leave one almost breathless. It was in 1877 that the Board of Trade had issued a circular to the railway companies impressing upon them the necessity of fitting *automatic* continuous brakes, whereupon Smith's Vacuum Brake Company issued a counterblast, calling the Government recommendations "unnecessary and inconsistent", and nearly two years later Sir Richard Moon told the L. & N.W.R. shareholders that "they heard a great deal about self-acting brakes, but he did not believe that any man in his senses would risk their trains to a self-acting brake". By self-acting, of course, he meant automatic. As yet, the Board of Trade had no legal right to enforce the fitting of automatic continuous brakes, and Colonel Yolland in reporting on a Midland smash near Wennington in 1880 said: "With the exception of a very few railway companies that recognised the necessity and acted upon it, it may be truly stated that the principal railway companies throughout the Kingdom have resisted the efforts of the Board of Trade to cause them to do what is right, which the latter had no legal power to enforce." It was not a very glorious period for the British railways, yet it had a close parallel in the shipping world at much the same time, when leading shipowners fought tooth and nail against the adoption of the Plimsoll line, which guarded against the overloading of ships.

"Resist" was a mild word to use in the circumstances.

But at length, after repeated accidents with the chain brake the London and North Western decided to change—but to the "simple" vacuum brake! The change was duly made notorious on the night of December 21st, 1886, when the down Limited Mail ran clean through Carlisle station, collided with a Midland engine, swept it aside, and ran for another 190 yards before it could be stopped. But it was on the Manchester, Sheffield and Lincolnshire that the most flagrant cases occurred. Using the simple vacuum brake there were bad accidents at Penistone in 1884 and again in 1886, and in reporting on the second of these General Hutchinson said: "It was very unsatisfactory to find that the Manchester, Sheffield and Lincolnshire Railway Company had done nothing towards supplying its rolling stock with automatic brakes, notwithstanding the warning it received from the very serious accident which occurred near Penistone in July 1884." Still no notice was taken, in fact the General Manager of another railway remarked: "I would prefer an occasional Penistone to being compelled by Government to put on something that I do not want." Then in September 1887 an even worse disaster occurred on the M.S. & L., at Hexthorpe, in which there was a heavy loss of life. As a result of this the driver and fireman of the express were tried for manslaughter at York Assizes, before the Lord Chief Justice of England. They were not merely acquitted, but the railway was found seriously to blame and severely censured by the Lord Chief Justice. And yet, at the very next meeting of the company, the chairman, Sir Edward Watkin, had the effrontery to say: "It was a misfortune that the Lord Chief Justice should have exonerated the driver and fireman."

The climax, so far as the "simple" vacuum brake, came in 1889, though not on the Manchester, Sheffield and Lincolnshire Railway. There is no point in re-telling, in all its ghastly details, the story of the runaway excursion train near Armagh, on the Great Northern Railway of Ireland, and of how ten packed coaches, entirely uncontrolled, came careering down a steep incline to crash into another train. Two facts were enough for public opinion: first, that of the 600-odd passengers in those ten coaches (mostly children), 78 were killed and 250 injured; secondly, that the train was

fitted with the simple vacuum brake. Confronted by such
a tragedy public reaction was swift enough, and before the
end of the year a Bill had been passed through Parliament
making automatic continuous brakes compulsory for all
passenger trains in this country.

With legislation imposed upon them, those companies that
had so vehemently opposed the Board of Trade, all adopted
the automatic vacuum, and so benefited from the development work that had been done on the Midland. But although
providing the safety features required by law it did not give
so good a performance as the Westinghouse, and in years
immediately after the passage of the Act various outside
interests continued to press the advantages of the air-brake.
But prejudice was deep-seated, and when one locomotive
superintendent was asked openly why he opposed the
Westinghouse he exclaimed: "I am an Englishman", and
that was that! On the Great Western the development of the
vacuum automatic brake came to provide a fascinating link
with the earliest days of railways, through the personality
of Joseph Armstrong, junior. Following the Midland lead
the Great Western took the Sanders and Bolitho brake; but
the locomotive superintendent of the day, William Dean,
instructed two of his cleverest assistants to "vet" the brake
in every detail; to redesign it where necessary, so as to
produce a thoroughly efficient, and quick-acting automatic
brake, while retaining the simplicity in operation inherent
in the vacuum. Those assistants were Armstrong, son of
Dean's immediate predecessor in the office of locomotive,
carriage and wagon superintendent, and a young Devonian
named George Jackson Churchward. To "Young Joe", as
Armstrong was affectionately known on the Great Western,
belongs most of the credit for producing by far the best
version of the vacuum automatic brake, but at this stage it
is interesting to turn back the pages of history for a moment
to recall the early connections of his family with the colliery
lines in Northumberland.

This book opened with the story of George Stephenson
proposing to emigrate. "Young Joe's" grandfather, Thomas
Armstrong, actually sold up, and sailed for Canada in 1817;
but things were no more settled in the New World than they

were in England, and in 1824 he returned to Northumberland. Joseph Armstrong the elder, was eight years old when his father and mother brought him and his brothers and sisters back to England, and while his father settled at Newburn-on-Tyne, near the Walbottle Colliery, Joseph was sent to Bruce's School, in Newcastle, where Robert Stephenson had been educated. When he was old enough he went to work at the Walbottle Colliery, under Robert Hawthorn, Stephenson's "great enemy". Later he met Timothy Hackworth, and there is reason to believe that Joseph Armstrong first sampled the art of engine-driving on the Stockton and Darlington line under Timothy's guidance. In 1836 at the age of twenty he went to the Liverpool and Manchester Railway as a driver. After moving with alacrity from one job to another, in the manner of the ambitious young locomotive engineers of the day, he came eventually into the service of the Great Western as northern division superintendent at Wolverhampton in 1854, and when Daniel Gooch retired in 1864, Armstrong succeeded him as locomotive superintendent of the entire system, with headquarters at Swindon.

In all, five members of this great railway family served the Great Western, and four had long and distinguished careers. It was ironical that the one who seemed to have the greatest mechanical genius in the family was killed on the line at Wolverhampton at the early age of thirty-one. This was "Young Joe", fourth son of he who succeeded Gooch as locomotive superintendent of the G.W.R. Joe Armstrong and Churchward together eliminated the running faults of the old Sanders and Bolitho brake. Originally an instrument known as an ejector was used for maintaining the vacuum in the continuous pipe running throughout the length of the train; this device, which works on the jet principle, used steam from the boiler, and the Great Western engineers felt that it did not give them a near enough approach to a perfect vacuum. The vacuum brake operates by the suction caused through a difference in pressure across a piston. As the pressure of the atmosphere is about $14\frac{3}{4}$ lb. per sq. in. this is the maximum difference one can expect if the opposite side of the piston is exhausted to a perfect vacuum. Ejectors in use were not able to give more than about two-thirds of a perfect vacuum, with a consequent difference in pressure of only 10 lb. per sq. in.

In developing the vacuum brake Armstrong introduced a curious reversal of the analogy between creating vacuum for the brakes and feeding water into the boiler. In earlier days a pump driven off the engine crosshead had been used for feeding the boiler, but this had been superseded by the steam injector; now for creation of vacuum Armstrong reverted to the crosshead pump, which not only used far less power when running, but enabled a considerably higher degree of vacuum to be maintained. He was able to maintain 26 or 27 in. of mercury (13 to $13\frac{1}{2}$ lb. per sq. in. pressure difference) against a maximum of about 21 in. with an ejector. In other words he provided about 30 per cent more power, and so gave Great Western passenger trains the best form of vacuum brakes in the country. Although this innovation was produced more than seventy years ago it is still standard on the Western Region today. As for his collaborator, G. J. Churchward, a whole book would be needed to cover the work he did subsequently for the Great Western, and for the town of Swindon, during the twenty years of his chieftainship of the locomotive department. It was due to one of his staff, the inimitable Conrad K. Dumas, that the vacuum brake was still further improved on the Great Western, and brought fully up to the standard of performance given by the air brake, at that time in the 1900's.

Reverting once again to the year 1889 a further contributory cause to the Armagh disaster had been the survival of the old "time interval" system of dispatching trains. This was abolished for good and all by the Act of 1889, which not only made the block system compulsory everywhere, but definitely specified the "closed block"—which, had it been in use of the Great Northern in 1876 might have saved the double collision at Abbots Ripton. The year 1889 was indeed a milestone in British Railway operation; but it is sad to recall that the safety principles on which the British Railways pride themselves today had to be *forced* on some of the leading companies from the bitter experience of so many accidents. Even with the passing of the Act of 1889 signalling was still a matter of working to a code of rules. While the interlocking between levers prevented the setting up of conflicting routes at stations or junctions there was still no positive interlocking between adjacent boxes, and nothing to stop a signalman from sending a second train forward before he had received clearance from the first. And now another great name in railway operating comes into the picture, to join those of Gregory, Saxby, Tyer, Deakin, and Westinghouse—the name of W. R. Sykes.

Railways had passed well beyond the Mania stage when W. R. Sykes got his first job, with the Electric Telegraph Company, as a youth of fourteen. That was in 1854. His duties were humble enough, and the hours were long, but not too long to prevent him devoting some time in the evenings to his abiding interest in clocks. With his spare pennies saved up he bought up old clocks, studied their mechanisms and repaired them, while between his multifarious duties as odd-job boy at the Telegraph Company he began to learn the rudiments of electricity. While in the service of the company, too, he came into contact with Thomas Varley, one of the pioneers of electric telegraphy and the latter in turn recognised in Sykes an industrious and ingenious mechanic. His chance came in 1862 when Mr. Rudall was appointed telegraph superintendent of the London, Chatham and Dover Railway; he needed a man to look after all the clocks and watches owned by the company and asked Varley if he could recommend someone. Varley immediately thought of Sykes, and so Sykes began a connection with railways that lasted for over fifty years. In addition to clocks, the block telegraph instruments came under his care, and with his broad outlook upon his job he was soon thinking out ways of improving the various means of communication between signal boxes. The outcome was the great invention of the "lock and block" system of working, of which the first installation was made at one of the busiest points in the whole metropolitan area at Canterbury Junction, Brixton.

In the environs of a station, or a main line junction there are many groups of signals for controlling various movements within the area for which the signalman is directly responsible; these are interlocked with one another, but the crux of the problem of regulating traffic along the line, between signal boxes, lay in the operation of the so-called "starting" signal. Once this was lowered the train was away to the next box and the signalman had no further control. The rules for operating were clear enough—that a train should not be allowed to proceed until the man in the box ahead agreed to accept it. But amid all the bustle of train working, block bells ringing, maybe four running lines to look after— which meant four sets of block instruments—a signalman might become confused and accept a train when the conditions were not safe for him to do so. Now, while Saxby, James Deakin and others had invented means for mechanically interlocking the levers with one another Sykes set himself the task of interlocking the levers *electrically* with the block instruments: not only this, but he sought to prove that the train was clear of the section before release could take place. To do this he had not only to work out a great principle of operation, but he had to invent two new forms of instrument: first, an electric lock that could be applied to a signal lever in a frame, and secondly an apparatus for registering the passage of a train.

In the Sykes "lock and block" system of working a signalman was positively prevented from lowering his starting signal until he received "line clear" from the man in the box next ahead; while, in turn, the man in the box ahead could not give the line clear release until the previous train had actually passed, and the starting signal for the next section ahead had been put to danger behind it. Experience was to show that even this degree of elaborate interlocking was not enough to block *all* the loopholes by which errors in train signalling could be made; yet it was a giant step forward, and it was adopted at an early stage by his old company, the London, Chatham and Dover. The management wanted to try it first at a quiet place in the country; but Sykes had such confidence in his apparatus that he persuaded them to install it on the busiest part of the whole line, the junctions in the neighbourhood of Brixton. While this trial was in progress there was a bad smash at Sittingbourne, and the decision was taken to equip the whole line with "lock and block". As a manufacturer Sykes began by renting a small shop in a railway arch at Nunhead; but as business began to

14

grow he obtained use of an old goods shed by the side of the London, Chatham and Dover line at Clapham, and when he received large orders for "lock and block" equipment from a number of the railways all the apparatus was made there. The firm he founded, the W. R. Sykes Interlocking Signal Company, flourishes today, on the same site, under the leadership of one of his grandsons.

The Sykes "lock and block" system was adopted by those railways that had very heavy suburban traffic in the London area—all the lines south of the Thames, and the Great Eastern running into Liverpool Street. It was noticeable that lines that had been most reluctant to adopt continuous automatic brakes were among those who did not adopt "lock and block". The system was devised solely to guard against the possibility of signalling errors, yet in the running of trains enginemen are as likely to make mistakes as signalmen. In the later years of the nineteenth century there were accidents due to the overrunning of signals as well as to errors in block working, and on certain railways the attention of locomotive engineers was turned towards the provision of some device that would assist drivers, particularly at times of bad visibility. The North Eastern was well to the fore in this particular movement, and it is perhaps rather significant that it was a line that was then using the best and most rapid-acting of brakes, should be seeking to improve running conditions still further. The North Eastern apparatus was introduced primarily to assist drivers in time of fog, and in principle it was strikingly similar to the "puppets" of Edward Bury used on the London and Birmingham Railway fifty years earlier.

On the North Eastern the earlier history of signalling itself was in some way repeated by this cab-signalling apparatus, in that the driver received an audible warning only when the signal was at danger. A striker arm was mounted in the middle of the track adjacent to each signal, and when the signal was in the danger position the arm was raised. As the locomotive passed a pendulum lever hit the striker, and the resulting movement caused a special whistle to sound in the cab. The various members combining to make up this apparatus were all carefully designed, and it worked well over a number of years; enginemen came to place complete reliance in its integrity, and it was common to see really fast running made in dense fog. In principle it was open to criticism on the grounds that if for any reason the striker gear was broken no indication would be given to the driver, and he would be justified in assuming all was clear, when in fact the signal might be at danger. Although no such case of failure was ever recorded the possibility was there all the same. Even so, the cab indications were analagous with those of the lineside signals used at the turn of the century. On the North Eastern white was still the night indication for "all clear" and the semaphore arms instead of having two spectacle glasses, as now, had only one—red. When the arm was lowered in the clear position the white light from the oil lamp was revealed. Thus if a red glass happened to get broken and fall out of its housing a "white" would be shown: an inherently dangerous condition. The moving spirit behind the introduction of the North Eastern cab signalling was Vincent Raven, the assistant locomotive superintendent, who afterwards became chief mechanical engineer.

The value of cab signalling cannot be over-emphasised. It is not only in fog or falling snow that it gives a driver a picture of the state of the line ahead; it is there at all times to supplement the indications given by the wayside signals. When running fast a second's hesitation in applying the brakes might, in emergency, mean all the difference between a safe stop and a collision. At 80 m.p.h. two seconds mean 100 yards! It would be bringing the story into the present century to discuss the further development of cab signalling, and its adjunct of automatic train control; but the need for it had been felt, and the North Eastern experiments date from 1896. Like "lock and block" it was not everywhere accepted as necessary, any more than automatic continuous brakes had been in earlier years; but with its original introduction, albeit in so imperfect a form, the great engineering features of operation that characterise British Railways today were all present at the end of the Victorian era. Great developments there certainly have been. The busiest suburban lines have been changed to electric traction; experiments are being made with new forms of motive power for main line haulage; colour light signals are very gradually

14*

replacing the old semaphores, and track circuits prove the
presence of trains on the line far more surely than the old
Sykes treadle bars. But the principles are unaltered, just as
those of the latest steam locomotives are very nearly "pure
Rocket".

In bringing this story of railway engineers towards its close
one looks back from the present time to what might be called
the seven ages of railways in this country. First, the days of
the pioneers, working up to the fury of the Mania; next the
years of disillusionment, of retrenchment, deceleration, and
hard times; and then came the troubled years, of accidents,
constant criticism, strikes, and the Battle of the Brakes.
From this period the railways emerged rather surprisingly to
the age of Edwardian affluence, when they were still the
pre-eminent means of travel by land. Then, the First War
period was followed by the realisation that traffic was
being lost to the roads; it was a time of economy, stunts,
and streamlining. The sixth age was perhaps the hardest of
all, as from the very outbreak of the Second World War
there was an almost complete embargo on capital expenditure,
with consequent deterioration. The seventh age is that of
the "new deal" which the British Railways have so long
been promised, and at last seem likely to get. What it will
bring remains to be seen.

The first age was pre-eminently that of the engineers. The
very existence of the lines at all was due to their efforts.
Once services were in operation maintenance of the permanent way, the building and enlarging of marshalling yards
and stations, with the occasional excitement of a washaway,
did not call for men of the same stamp as Robert Stephenson,
or Brunel. Similarly in locomotive engineering, once the
pioneer stages were passed repairs and maintenance, together
with staff problems on the running side, occupied most of
the time of those who were superintendents during the later
part of the Victorian era. The surviving veterans of early
days realised this, and Olinthus J. Vignoles ended the
biography of his father with this unequivocal sentence: "With
C. B. Vignoles the romantic age of engineering science may
be said to have passed away." The date of that biography

was 1889, a sombre year in the history of railways. The world had yet to hear of Charles Parsons, of Royce, of Frank Whittle, and Marconi; but even in the everyday field of railway operating there have been moments in this twentieth century when the world has stood by to cheer, not perhaps in such numbers, but certainly with more understanding and genuine enthusiasm than that of the gapers who thronged to see George Stephenson's first efforts. There was a flash of that blazing pioneer spirit when the once disreputable Manchester, Sheffield and Lincolnshire decided to extend their line to London, and under the finer and more appropriate title of Great Central Railway to challenge on equal terms the three well-established trunk lines running from London to the North. There was another flash, when the Great Western not only set up Fishguard as an Irish packet station in flagrant opposition to the Royal Mail route via Holyhead, but also tapped the London and North Western gold mine in the ocean traffic to North America, via Liverpool.

In the twentieth century, for all except the first decade railway engineers have had a thankless task. But much of the year-to-year spade work to keep the trains running would have had the warm appraisal of pioneers like Vignoles, and Locke who both had a well-developed sense of human values. Both those permanent-way designers would, one feels sure, have been fascinated by the way the track has been fettled up, since the end of the Second World War, to its old standards despite a grievous shortage of men and materials: of how new tools have been introduced; how the depleted gangs have been trained in the use of them, so that on Brunel's old road at any rate, from 1953 onwards over lengthy stretches, the service timetable could state: "The speed may be as high as necessary . . .", and that sometimes means 100 m.p.h., or more. Trial trips with engines newly repaired are often little more than a formality; a gentle spin down the line running light, and that is all. But there was a works manager at Swindon not so many years ago who used to take the largest express engine personally, and there were no mild "toddles" where he was concerned. Shades of Nicholas Wood, and his evidence before the Gauge Commissioners! Repaired engines were taken up to 100 m.p.h. or more, until one day

14**

as they tore by, a signalman caught sight of a bowler hat on
the engine and hastily 'phoned ahead to have them stopped
at all costs. "A dangerous lunatic in plain clothes had," he
averred, "seized control of the engine"!

Among twentieth century railway engineers the name of
H. N. Gresley will always be outstanding, and in the nineteen thirties while he was chief mechanical engineer to the
London and North Eastern Railway it was indeed as though
the romantic age of railways had returned. He built a
colossal engine for service in Scotland, the *Cock o' the North*,
and as if to chide British railway managements for not having
a modern testing plant sent his engine to France to run trials.
The German State Railways put on the very fast diesel train
The Flying Hamburger; Gresley examined the possibilities of
such a service between Kings Cross and Newcastle, but found
he could do considerably better with one of his own engines.
That, however, was not good enough for the Silver Jubilee
year of his Majesty King George V. Shades of Sturrock!
Doncaster works was once again put to an extreme case of
constructional speed, and in the short space of five months
they had designed and built the streamlined Silver Jubilee
train. On its very first run it beat every speed record ever
made in British railway history; and when this train earned
for its designer a well-merited knighthood the man who the
railway world had hitherto known as Herbert N. Gresley
took as his title that borne by the ancestor that fought with
King Henry V at Agincourt—Sir Nigel Gresley. Who said
the romantic age of railways was ended!

One stormy night in the late autumn of last year I was
travelling from Bristol to London; and the journey on which
we averaged nearly 70 m.p.h. from start to stop, seemed to
epitomise the labours of railway engineers from the pioneer
days until now. We travelled over Brunel's famous road,
with an engine that was Stephenson in principle, though
adapted and enlarged to present day needs by the genius of
Churchward and his successors at Swindon. Most of the rails
over which we ran were of Locke's basic design, though some
of the newest put in were Vignoles. The signals were controlled by a modern form of "lock and block", and the driver
had audible signals and automatic train control in his cab.

Outside the wind howled, and the rain lashed the sides of the carriages, yet we sped on, as on the fairest summer day, with speed rising at one point to 95 m.p.h. But such speeds are nothing out of the ordinary today on *The Bristolian*, and the smoothness of the riding was never more pronounced than at the one moment when an adverse signal was sighted in the distance, and Joe Armstrong's brake came into action. Swiftly, and without the slightest jolt, speed was checked from 80 m.p.h. down to 20 m.p.h. There was a feeling of great security in that fast train, and inevitably one's thoughts went back to the words of Brunel: "I shall not attempt to argue with those who consider any increase in speed unnecessary. The public will always prefer that conveyance which is the most perfect; and speed, within reasonable limits, is a material ingredient in perfection of travelling."

INDEX

Numerals in **heavy type** refer to the *figure numbers* of illustrations.

Accidents:
  Abbots Ripton, 235, 243
  Armagh, 240
  Carlisle, 240
  Greenwich boiler explosion, 31
  Harrow, 221
  Hexthorpe, 240
  Nine Elms, 221
  Parkside, 216
  Penistone, 240
  Sittingbourne, 245
  Wennington, 239
Atmospheric System:
  Artistic engine-houses, 145
  Brunel's advocacy, 142
  Dublin and Kingstown, 141
  Failure in S. Devon, 143
  London and Croydon, 141, 144
  The Principle, 140; **54, 55**
  Proposal for Newcastle and Berwick, 154, 166
  Rennie's views, 143
  South Devon, 141

Bath Station, **28**
Battle of Bergen-op-Zoom, 54
Board of Trade Inspecting Officers:
  Hutchinson, Maj.-Gen., 240
  Pasley, Gen., 154, 177, 181
  Recommendations on brakes, 239
  Rich, Col., 229
  Smith, Sir F., 101, 141, 221
  Value of Inspectorate, 215, 230
  Yolland, Col., 226, 239
Brakes:
  Battle of the brakes, 238
  Clark and Webb, 234, 237
  Newark trials, 234
  Reluctance of companies to adopt, 233, 230
  Vacuum (automatic), 241, 242
  Vacuum (G.W. development), 242
  Vacuum (simple), 234, 239
  Westinghouse, 233, 241
Branch Lines:
  Sir C. H. Gregory's views, 223
Bridges:
  Bathford, **14**
  Britannia (tubular), 193 *et seq.*; **7, 47, 49, 50**
  Conway (tubular), 193 *et seq.*; **44, 48**

Foord Viaduct, 181
Fox's Wood, **58**
High Level, viaduct, **40**
Middlesborough (near), **4**
Newcastle (High Level), 168 *et seq.*
Penkridge, 93, 97
Penmaenmawr, 197, 198
Royal Border, 173
Saltash, 205; **29, 30**
Sankey, 93
Skew, Bath, **59**
Timber (South Devon Line), 199
Bridgwater Canal, 68, 72
Bristolian, The, 251
Brunel, Isambard Kingdom, work of:
  Thames tunnel, 111
  Suspension bridge at Bristol, 111
  Engineer of the G.W.R., 111
  The broad gauge, 112; **28**
  Form of permanent way, 115
  Changing the White Horse, 116
  Ordering the first locomotives, 131
  Gooch, his loco. assistant, 132; **37, 39**
  Preference to the *North Star,* 133
  Difficulties with early engines, 134
  Tribute from Gauge Commission, 155
  South Devon viaducts, 200; **52, 53**
  Maintaining the viaducts, 200; **52, 53**
  Royal Albert Bridge, 205; **29, 30**
  His death, 205

Cab Signalling:
  Bury's, 221
  Raven's on N.E.R., 246
Camden, Engine house at, **20**
Cornish Pumping Engines:
  Newcomen's, 20
  Separate condenser, 25
  Trevithick's high pressure, 27
  Watt's work 24
  Watt's method of payment for, 26
  "Wheal Busy", 25
Crewe Station, **27**

Engineers:
  Allan, A., 129, 155
  Allcard, W., 78, 156
  Armstrong, J., 241
  Armstrong, J. (Jun.), 241, 242
  Bidder, G. P., 147, 151, 167

Engineers: (*contd.*)
Birkenshaw, 62
Blenkinsop, 40
Booth, H., 122
Boulton, M., 25
Braithwaite, J., 121, 173
Brassey, T., 92 *et seq.*, 101; 19
Brunel, Sir M., 37, 51
Brunel, I. K., 51, 110, 111 *et seq.*, 199; 1
Buddicom, E., 155
Bury, E., 137, 221
Chambers, A., 226
Churchward, G. J., 241, 250
Crampton, T., 130, 135
Cubitt, W., 141, 149, 180, 185; 61
Deakin family, 224 *et seq.*, 230
Dixon, J., 57, 65, 78
Dodds, Isaac, 47
Ericcson, 121
Fletcher, E., 83, 129
Giles, F., 73, 80, 98
Gooch, D., 130, 132, 136, 149, 152, 153; 37, 39
Gregory, C. H., 222
Gresley, Sir N., 250
Hackworth, T., 66, 84, 117, 127, 129, 242; 31, 32
Hawthorn, R., 42, 131
Howe, W., 139
James, W., 36, 67, 69, 81
Jessop, W., 17
Joy, D., 149, 158
Locke, J., 43, 78, 91, 94, 111, 155, 165, 173, 185, 215; 18
McConnell, J. E., 158, 159
Murray, M., 40
Newcomen, T., 19
Raven, V. L., 247
Ramsbottom, J., 129, 162, 163
Rastrick, J. U., 87
Rennie, G., 52
Rennie, J., 38, 52
Rennie, Sir J. (Jun.), 52, 54, 67, 73, 74, 76, 103, 157
Savery, T., 20
Saxby, J., 225, 227; 65
Sinclair, R., 130, 156
Smeaton, T., 54
Steele, J., 35, 43
Stephenson, G., 15, 35, 40, 41 *et seq.*, 55, 57, 67, 165; 2
Stephenson, R., 57, 65, 83, 105, 137, 165; 10
Stevens, J., 224
Sturrock, A., 130, 133, 156, 160, 161
Sykes, W. R., 224
Telford, T., 38, 54; 46

Trevithick, R., 27, 29, 36, 118
Tyer, E., 231
Vignoles, C. B., 54, 67, 75, 76, 77, 115, 121, 173, 207, 208; 62
Watt, J., 23 *et seq.*
Westinghouse, G., 232 *et seq.*; 64
Wood, N., 43, 55, 176; 3
Engineering Works:
Blisworth Cutting, 104; 23
Chat Moss, 71, 75, 78
Fareham Cutting, 101
Folkestone Warren, 181
Olive Mount Cutting, 80; 11
Organisation of earthworks, 94, 97
Penmaenmawr, 197, 198; 51
Viaducts, on Falmouth line, 52, 53
Exeter expresses, 136

Gauge Commission: 145
Evidence of Brunel, 146, 151
Evidence of Daniel Gooch, 149
Evidence of Locke, 146
Evidence of Stephenson, 146
Evidence of Nicholas Wood, 150
Gauges, various, 110

Institution of Civil Engineers:
Attitude to G. Stephenson, 157
Locke's Presidency, 199
Telford's influence, 53
Vignoles's Presidency, 77, 208
Institution of Mechanical Engineers, 158
Irish Mail Route:
Chester and Holyhead proposal, 187
Crossing the Straits, 188; 46
Port Dinlleyn, 186
Stephenson *versus* Brunel, 187

Leighton Buzzard, Rock blasting near, 15
Liverpool and Manchester opening, 215 *et seq.*
Locomotives:
Actæon, 136, 142
Allan's type, 156
Beattie Express, 35
Blenkinsop, 40
Bloomer, 159
Buddicom's type, 156
Bury's type, 137; 42
Crampton's, 158
Derwent, 119
DX Goods, 162
Firefly, 135
Fountains Hall, 140
Great A, 151, 152; 38
Great Western, 153; 39
Invicta, 83

Locomotives: (contd.)
  Ixion, 151, 154
  Killingworth type, 44, 51
  King Edward VII, 128
  Jenny Lind, 160
  Liverpool, 159
  Locomotion, 66
  Metropolitan-type, 161
  Newcastle, 5
  North Eastern compound, 128
  North Star, 133
  Novelty, 121; 33
  Penydaren, 32; 5
  Prince of Wales, 137
  Richmond, 137
  Rocket, 88, 117, 123, 128; 34
  Royal George, 85, 118; 31
  Sans Pareil, 120; 32
  Sinclair, 41
  White Horse of Kent, 149, 155
  Wylam types, 44
Locomotive design:
  Blast pipe, 47, 118, 119, 134
  Boiler flues, 119, 122
  Brick arch, 162
  Condensing, 161
  Crank axles, 155
  Fuels, 161
  Link motion, 138, 165
  Long-boiler (Stephenson), 137, 155
  Reversing, Gears, 138-9, 162
  Riding qualities, 159
  Toothed wheels, 40
  Wheels, (early types), 119

Mania, 157, 180
  Effects on engineers, 164, 207
Menai Straits, Bridges, 46
Metropolitan Railway, 160

Navvies:
  At Furness Abbey, 180
  At Kilsby Tunnel, 106
  French interest, 96
  Organisation, 95
  Rev. W. E. Dickson's view, 96

Penydaren trials, 33, 34
Personalities:
  Boulton, Matthew, 25
  Denison, Edmund, 185
  Fenton, Miles, 160
  Giddy, Davies, 28
  Gill, T., 143
  Homfray, Samuel, 31
  Hudson, George, 150
  Lord Alderson, 73
  Lord Howick, 166
  Lord Lowther, 74

  Lord Ravensworth, 44
  Lord Wharncliffe, 175
  Moon, Richard, 237
  Pease, Edward, 56, 84, 86
Press antagonism, 102

Queen Victoria at High Level Bridge, 172

Rails:
  Birkinshaw, 62
  Blenkinsop, 40
  Jessop, 17
  Locke, 110, 207
  Plate type, 17
  Stephenson and Losh, 48, 62; 8
  Vignoles, 109, 208
Railway books:
  Autobiography of Sir John Rennie, 53, 73, 74
  Biographies (Samuel Smiles), 49, 68, 106, 121, 165
  Devey's Life of Joseph Locke, 179
  Evolution of Railways (Chas. E. Lee), 16
  History of Southern Railway (Marshall), 145
  Life of Telford (Sir Alexander Gibb), 54
  Life of C. B. Vignoles (O. J. Vignoles), 248
  Rambles on the Railway (Roney), 163
  Timothy Hackworth and the Locomotive (R. Young), 124 et seq.
  Wood's Treatise on Railroads, 121
Rainhill trials: 88
  Conditions of test, 120
  Design of the Rocket, 122; 34
  Failure of the Sans Pareil, 125; 32
  Further trials of the Novelty, 127
  Hackworth enters, 119
  The judges, 121
  The Novelty entered, 121; 33
  Speed of the Novelty, 122
  The Stephensons' win, 126
  Vignoles's account, 123
  Wood's description, 124
Rope worked inclines, 65
Routes:
  Bodmin and Wadebridge, 102
  Brighton, 224
  Bristol and Exeter, 135; 36
  Caledonian, 156
  Canterbury and Whitstable, 82
  Chester and Holyhead, 141, 197
  Cornwall, 205
  Eastern Counties, 146, 173
  Festiniog, 102
  Glasgow and Berwick, 37

Routes: (*contd.*)
 Grand Junction, 91, 94
 Great Northern, 160, 185
 Great Western, 91; **28**
 Hetton Colliery, 50
 Kendal and Windermere, 179
 Lancaster and Carlisle, 178
 Leeds and Selby, 102
 Liverpool and Manchester, 70 *et seq.*
 London and Birmingham, 91, 102
 London, Chatham and Dover, 244
 London and Croydon, 144
 London and Greenwich, 102
 London and North Western, 156,
  198; **27**
 London and Southampton, 91, 98,
  101
 Manchester and Birmingham Rail-
  way, **6**
 Manchester and Leeds Railway, **9**
 Manchester and Sheffield, 102, 173
 Midland, 108
 Midland Counties, 109
 Newcastle and Berwick, 167
 Newcastle and Carlisle, 102
 North Eastern, 224
 North Midland, 91, 107, 231; **25**
 South Devon, 142; **54, 55**
 South Eastern, 180
 Stockton and Darlington, 56, 58 *et
  seq.*, 65; **4**
 Surrey Iron Railroad, 18
 Wylam Colliery, 44

Sankey Viaduct, **17**
Signalling:
 Banister's semaphores, 224
 Block working (G.N.R.), 235
 Bury's puppets, 221
 Cab signalling, 221
 Closed block, 231, 243
 Corbett's Lane Lighthouse, 220
 Early attempts, 219
 "Hole in the Wall" signal box, **63**
 Interlocking, 226
 Junction working, 222
 Lamps (Saxby), 225
 Lock and Block, 244
 McKenzie and Holland, 230
 Posts (Stevens), 224
 Telegraph, 231
 Time interval, 235, 243
Stephenson, George, work of:
 His business acumen, 58
 Appreciation of industrial strategy,
  59
 Travelling by 'nip', 60
 His first public assignment, 61
 Surveying, 62

 His prophecy, in 1835, 66
 Opening of Stockton and Darlington
  line, 66
 Hostility to surveyors, 68
 Liverpool and Manchester surveys,
  70
 Chat Moss surveys, 71
 Speed of travel, 72
 Sketchy view of bridges, etc., **73**
 Examination in Committee, 73
 Engineer to Liverpool and Man-
  chester Railway, 76
 Chat Moss troubles, 78 *et seq.*
 Position of his assistants, 80
 Errors in Edge Hill survey, 81
 Championship of the steam loco-
  motive, 85
 Costs of railway haulage, 87
 Estrangement from Locke, 94
 North Midland line, 107
 Colliery owner, 107
 Limekilns at Ambergate, 107, 108;
  26
 Lord Howick and the Atmospheric,
  166
 Wrestling matches, 167
 His death, 195

Trackways (early):
 Plate-ways, 17
 Roman rut-ways, 16, 17
 Surrey Iron, 18
Train resistance tests (Stephenson
  and Wood), 50
Trevithick's road carriage, 30, 31
Tubular bridges:
 Conway, 193, 195
 Dickson's description, 196
 Friendly volunteer assistants, 195
 Menai Strait, 193
Tunnels:
 Abbots Cliff, 182; **43**
 Box, **56**
 Edge Hill, 80
 Fareham, 101
 Kilsby, 104 *et seq.*; **22, 24**
 Martello, 182
 Penmaenmawr, 197; **51**
 St. Anne's, **57**
 Shakespeare's Cliff, 182; **45**
 The shield, 52
 Tyler's Hill, 82
 Ventilating shafts, 106
 Watford, **21**
 Woodhead, 174, 176, 211–2

Water troughs, 129, 162
Wharncliffe Viaduct, **60**
Wolverton embankment, **16**